THE
CITY OF GOD
Saint Augustine

STUDENT STUDY GUIDE

by Dr. David Charlton

© 2010 Memoria Press
ISBN 978-1-61538-122-7

Cover design and lay-out by Karah Force
Memoria Press
www.memoriapress.com

Few books receive more than one printing. A fortunate few may receive a second printing and an even fewer number receive multiple reprints. The reason for this is simple; most books have a life-span of a few years at best, finding an audience for a time until a lack of interest or irrelevancy pushes them out of print.

Then there is the small number of books that achieve the elite status of classic. When you think of classic literature a select group of authors immediately comes to mind – Shakespeare, Milton, Dante, and a handful of others who gave the world timeless classics to be studied as long as mankind populates the earth. But even among the classics there are the few authors whose literary greatness shapes the very course of a civilization.

To such a class belongs Augustine. Possessing one of the most brilliant minds in the history of Western civilization, Augustine penned the *City of God*, a book that influenced society more powerfully than perhaps any other book except the Bible. The *City of God* is a monumental work in which Augustine presents his view of two cities – the spiritual *City of God* and the *Earthly City*.

As is often the case, great literature is born of struggle. Augustine wrote the *City of God* in response to the charge that Christianity had weakened the mighty Roman Empire and was the cause for its tragic decline. Augustine's powerful rebuttal of this charge rose out of the struggle between the spiritual and the temporal that battled for the heart of the Empire.

To study the *City of God* is to study the source of some of Western society's greatest and most cherished beliefs. This is the source that serves as the fountainhead of all that followed, and it is unlikely that it will ever be equaled.

If the beauty of this order fails to delight us, it is because we ourselves, by reason of our mortality, are so enmeshed in this corner of the cosmos that we fail to perceive the beauty of a total pattern in which the particular parts, which seem ugly to us, blend in so harmonious and beautiful a way. That is why, in those situations where it is beyond our power to understand the providence of God, we are rightly commanded to make an act of faith rather than allow the rashness of human vanity to criticize even a minute detail in the masterpiece of our Creator.

Book XII, Chapter 4, ¶ 2

Meet Augustine

1. To study Augustine is to study _____, which comes from the Greek word

   _____, which means _____.

2. Augustine was born in the year ___354 AD___ in the city of

   ___Thagaste___ in ___Africa___.

3. His father ___Patricius___ was a ___pagan___ and his mother

   ___Monica___ was a ___Catholic___.

4. At age _____ Augustine was sent to school at _____,

   where he became familiar with _____ literature, as well as

   _____ beliefs and _____.

5. At age _____ Augustine went to _____ to continue his

   education in _____.

6. At age _____ Augustine read Cicero's _____, which he

   described as leaving a lasting impression on him and sparking his interest in _____.

7. Although raised a _____ Augustine left the Church to follow the controversial

   _____ religion.

8. The Manichaeans were founded by _____, who was born in

   _____ in _____. It was based on Persian

   _____ and was very _____. It was very similar to the

   beliefs of _____ and had a simple worship but very strict

   _____.

9. When Augustine came to _____ he was very influenced by the preaching of

   _____.

Meet Augustine

10. Augustine came to be aware of the great difference between his _____ and his

    _____. He was very impressed by the _____ life, and the

    thought that these _____ men could overcome what he, as a

    _____ man could not led to a crisis in his life.

11. Augustine was converted in _____ and became a _____.

12. In _____ Augustine was consecrated bishop of _____ and

    spent the last _____ years of his life there.

13. In the year _____ the _____ leader

    _____ captured the city of _____. Though it was a case of

    a _____ leader capturing a _____ city, the

    _____ were alarmed and blamed the _____.

14. This was not the first time the Christians had been blamed for the problems of

    _____. The emperor _____ had blamed the Christians

    for a _____ that _____ much of Rome.

15. Augustine wrote the *City of God* at the request of _____. The book was a

    _____ of _____.

16. The first sections of the *City of God* appeared around _____ and continued to be

    published over the next _____ years or so.

17. The two cities in the *City of God* are the _____ and the

    _____, also known as _____.

18. The Latin title of the *City of God* is _____.

The Influence of Augustine

1. Augustine made a careful comparison between _____ society and

   _____ belief.

2. Augustine provided unity of _____ at a time when the church was threatened with

   division.

3. The *City of God* provided a _____ for the _____ of the

   church in the world.

4. The source of many of Western society's most enduring _____ and

   _____ can be traced to Augustine. Among them are the idea of the

   _____ of _____ and _____.

5. Augustine's view of _____ is still very dominant today.

6. The concept of _____ _____, especially as found in the

   _____ _____ theory. This theory states that to be

   justifiable, a war must have a _____, a _____,

   _____, a _____, must use _____,

   and must be used only as a _____.

7. Augustine strongly influenced the Church's concept of _____

   _____.

8. The _____ and its emphasis on _____ owes a great debt to

   Augustine.

9. Augustine injected a strong sense of _____ into society. Christianity entered a

   world that was very _____. Augustine envisioned a world of

   _____.

Focus Passages

Book I, Chapter 3, (page 44) –

These men, I say, hold Christ responsible for the evils which they deservedly suffer for their wicked lives. They have not the slightest appreciation of the fact, that, when they deserved to be punished, they were spared for Christ's sake. On the contrary, with impious perversity and bitterness, they attack His Name with those very tongues which falsely invoked that Name to save them. The very tongues which, like cowards, they held in check in the sacred places when safe, protected and unharmed by the enemy for Christ's sake, they now use to hurl malicious curses against Him.

Book I, Chapter 8 (pages 45-46) –

However, there is a vast difference between the manner in which men use what we call prosperity and adversity. A good man is neither puffed up by fleeting success nor broken by adversity; whereas, a bad man is chastised by failure of this sort because he is corrupted by success. God often shows His intervention more clearly by the way He apportions the sweet and the bitter. For, if He visited every sin here below with manifest penalty, it might be thought that no score remained to be settled at the Last Judgment. On the other hand, if God did not plainly enough punish sin on earth, people might conclude that there is no such thing as Divine Providence. So, too, in regard to the good things of life. If God did not bestow them with patent liberality on some who ask Him, we could possibly argue that such things did not depend on His power. On the other hand, if He lavished them on all who asked, we might have the impression that God is to be served only for the gifts He bestows. In that case, the service of God would not make us religious, but rather covetous and greedy. In view of all that, when good and bad men suffer alike, they are not, for that reason indistinguishable because what they suffer is similar. The sufferers are different even though the sufferings are the same trials; though what they endure is the same, their virtue and vice are different.

For, in the same fire, gold gleams and straw smokes; under the same flail the stalk is crushed and the grain threshed; the lees are not mistaken for oil because they have issued from the same press. So, too, the tide of trouble will test, purify, and improve the good, but beat, crush, and wash away the wicked. So it is that, under the weight of the same affliction, the wicked deny and blaspheme God, and the good pray to Him and praise Him. The difference is not in what people suffer but in the way they suffer. The same shaking that makes fetid water stink makes perfume issue a more pleasant odor.

Book I, Chapter 21 (page 57) –

The same divine law which forbids the killing of a human being allows certain exceptions, as when God authorizes killing by a general law or when He gives an explicit commission to an individual for a limited time. Since the agent of authority is but a sword in the hand, and is not responsible for the killing, it is in no way contrary to the commandment, "Thou shalt not kill," to wage war at God's bidding, or for the representatives of the State's authority to put criminals to death, according to the law or the rule of rational justice.

Thus, Abraham was not only free from the guilt of criminal cruelty, but even commended for his piety, when he consented to sacrifice his son, not, indeed, with criminal intent but in obedience to God. One may well ask, also, whether it was not God's command that Jephte killed his daughter when she met him after he vowed that he would sacrifice to God the first thing he encountered, if he returned victorious from battle. Samson crushed himself and his enemies to death beneath the ruins of a building. He can only be excused on the grounds that the Spirit of the Lord, who wrought miracles through him, had bidden him to do so. But, apart from such men excepted by the command of a just law in general or of God, the very Source of justice, in a special case, anyone who kills a human being, himself or another, is guilty of murder.

Chapter Summarization

Preface

_____

_____

_____

_____

Chapter 1

_____

_____

_____

_____

Chapter 8

_____

_____

_____

_____

Chapter 9

_____

_____

_____

_____

Chapter Summarization

Chapter 19

_____

_____

_____

_____

Chapter 21

_____

_____

_____

_____

Chapter 27

_____

_____

_____

_____

Chapter 36

_____

_____

_____

_____

Comprehension Questions

1. In chapter one Augustine is criticizing the enemies of the City of God. What is the criticism he is leveling against them?

2. Summarize Augustine's point about suffering in chapter eight.

3. In chapter nine Augustine criticizes Christians for not reproving the wicked. Why, in Augustine's opinion, have Christians failed to do this?

4. In chapter nineteen Augustine presents the case of Lucretia, who committed suicide. What reason does Augustine give for her suicide?

5. According to chapter twenty-one, does Augustine ever see a justifiable reason for killing another human being. If so, what is the reason or reasons?

6. In chapter twenty-seven Augustine says there may be only one justifiable reason for suicide. What is that reason and does he ultimately agree with it?

7. In chapter thirty-three Augustine gives a strongly worded reason for why Rome suffered the humiliation of defeat. Describe what Augustine has to say.

Vocabulary

I shall consider it both in its **temporal** stage here below (where it journeys as a pilgrim among sinners and lives by faith) and as solidly established in its eternal abode – that blessed goal for which we patiently hope "until justice be turned into judgment," but which, one day is to be the reward of excellence in a final victory and a perfect peace.

Preface, ¶ 1, line 5

To this both the shrines of the martyrs and the basilicas of the Apostles bear witness: amid the city's devastation, these buildings gave refuge not only to the faithful but even to the **infidels**.

Chapter 1, ¶ 2, line 5

Yet, if they only had sense, they would see that the hardships and cruelties they suffered from the enemy came from that **Divine Providence** who makes use of war to reform the corrupt lives of men.

Chapter 1, ¶ 2, line 21

Let the **pagans** read these chronicles, and then adduce one single instance of a city falling into the hands of a foe disposed to spare men seeking refuge in the temples of their gods.

Chapter 2, ¶ 1, line 3

For, although some who reflect on these truths repent and are converted from their wickedness, others, according to the words of the Apostle, despise "the riches of His goodness and long-suffering, in the hardness of their heart and **impenitence**" and treasure up to themselves "wrath against the day of wrath and revelation of the just judgment of God Who will render to every man according to his works.

Chapter 8, ¶ 1, line 9

The fact is that everyone, however exemplary, yields to some promptings of **concupiscence**: if not to monstrous crimes, abysmal villainy, and abominable impiety, at least some sins, however rarely or – if frequently – however venially.

Chapter 9, ¶ 1, line 10

For, his example shows that the gods are utterly useless to secure temporal **felicity** for their worshippers.

Chapter 15, ¶ 2, line 9

To my **cogent** argument to this effect, some may venture to take exception.

Chapter 19, ¶ 1, line 4

Since the agent of authority is but a sword in the hand, and is not responsible for the killing, it is in no way contrary to the commandment, "Thou shalt not kill," to wage war at God's bidding, or for the representatives of the **State's** authority to put criminals to death, according to law or the rule of rational justice.

Chapter 21, ¶ 1, line 8

Vocabulary – Write the vocabulary word on the first line (a help for spelling) followed by the definition.

1. Temporal

   _____. _____

   _____.

2. Infidels

   _____. _____

   _____.

3. Divine Providence

   _____. _____

   _____.

4. Pagans

   _____. _____

   _____.

5. Impenitence

   _____. _____

   _____.

6. Concupiscence

   _____. _____

   _____.

7. Felicity

   _____. _____

   _____.

8. Cogent

   _____. _____

   _____.

9. State's

   _____. _____

   _____.

Memorable Quote

For in the same fire, gold gleams and straw smokes; under the same flail the stalk is crushed and the grain threshed; the lees are not mistaken for oil because they have issued from the same press. So, too, the tide of trouble will test, purify, and improve the good, but beat, crush, and wash away the wicked. So it is that, under the weight of the same affliction, the wicked deny and blaspheme God, and the good pray to Him and praise Him. The difference is not in what people suffer but in the way they suffer. The same shaking that makes fetid water stink makes perfume issue a more pleasant odor.

Chapter 8 ¶ 3, page 46

Focus Passages

Book II, Chapter 1, (page 66) –

If man's sickly understanding would not set plain truth at defiance, but humbly submit this common infirmity to the tonic of wholesome doctrine until, by filial trust in God's help, it regained its strength, those who think straight and express their thoughts in well-chosen speech would have no need of many words to correct the errors of baseless assumption. Unfortunately, however, there prevails a major and malignant malady of fools, the victims of which mistake their irrational impulses for truth and reason, even when confronted with as much evidence as any man has a right to expect from another. It may be an excess of blindness which prevents them from seeing the most glaring facts, or a perverse obstinacy which prevents them from accepting the facts when seen. This compels me to present more diffusely, not for their closed eyes to see, but, so to speak, for their hands to touch and feel, some obvious points.

Yet, if we always felt obliged to reply to counterstatements, when would there be an end to the argument or a limit to discussion? For, those who cannot grasp what is said, or, if they understand the truth, are too obdurate to accept it, keep on replying and, according to Holy Writ, 'speak iniquity' and never weary of empty words. You can easily see what an endless, wearisome, and fruitless task it would be, if I were to refute all the unconsidered objections of people who pigheadedly contradict everything I say.

Book II, Chapter 4, (page 69) –

In the first place, why were the gods so negligent as to allow the morals of their worshipers to sink to so low a depth? The true God leaves those who do not worship Him to their own devices, but why did not those gods (whose worship, so thankless men complain, is forbidden) lay down moral precepts that would help their devotees to lead a decent life? They should have had as much concern for their worshippers' conduct as these had for their cult. But, some one will reply, each man is bad by his own will. No one ever denied this! Nevertheless, it was incumbent on protecting deities, not to conceal from their worshipers the laws of a good life, but to proclaim such laws from the housetops. It was for them to seek out and call sinners to task through the medium of prophets whose duty it was to threaten evil-doers with the punishment awaiting them, and to hold out the promise of reward for virtuous living.

Book II, Chapter 21, (pages 74-75) –

When, therefore, the Roman republic was such as Sallust describes it, it was not only 'very wicked and corrupt' – 'a sink of iniquity,' as he puts it – it was no republic at all, if measured by the criterion established by its ablest representatives when they met to debate the nature of a republic.

Tullius himself, at the beginning of his fifth book, quotes the verse of the poet Ennius declaring: "The Roman state rests on the men and the morals of old,' and in his own words, not those of Scipio or any other, remarks: "That line for its conciseness and truth sound to me like the utterance of an oracle. For, had not the state been blessed with a wholesome body of citizens, and had not those men stood at the head, neither men nor morals could have availed to found or so long maintain a republic of such might to rule so far and wide and so justly. Indeed, long before our time, it was the custom of the land to appoint distinguished men who held fast to the ancient traditions and the institutions of our forefathers. Our own generation inherited the republic, an exquisite masterpiece, indeed, though faded with age; but it failed to restore its original colors. Worse, alas; it did not even move a finger to preserve as much as its form, or its barest outlines.

What is there left of the ancient virtue which the illustrious poet Ennius declared was the mainstay of the Roman state? We are aware only that it has been so utterly cast to the winds that morals are not merely unobserved, but are positively ignored. What can we say of the men? Precisely for want of men the good old customs have been lost, and for so great an evil not only are we responsible but we should face judgment, like

Focus Passages

culprits fearing the penalty of death. By our own vices, not by chance, we have lost the republic, though we retain the name.'

Book II, Chapter 29 (pages 76-77) –

But, it is now day; awake as you awoke in the persons of those men in whose sterling virtue and sufferings for the faith we glory. They battled on all sides against hostile powers and, conquering by their fearless death, 'have purchased this country for us with their blood.' To this Country we pleadingly invite you. Join its citizens, for it offers more than mere sanctuary, it offers the true remission of your sins.

Give no heed to the degenerate progeny who blame Christ and Christians for what they call bad times, and long for times which assure them, not a peaceful life, but undisturbed wickedness. Such times were never to your liking, not even for an earthly fatherland. Reach out now for the heavenly country. You will have very little to suffer for it, and in it you will reign in very truth, and forever. In that land there is not Vestal altar, no statue of Jupiter on the Capitol, but the one true God, who 'will not limit you in space or time, but will give an empire universal and eternal.' Seek no false and lying gods; rather, cast them from you with scorn and shine forth in true freedom. They are not gods, but fiendish spirits, to whom your eternal happiness is a torment. Never did Juno so intensely begrudge the Trojans, your ancestors in the flesh, the battlements of Rome, as do those demons, whom you still fancy to be gods, begrudge an everlasting home to the whole human race.

Chapter Summarization

Chapter 1

_____

_____

_____

_____

Chapter 2

_____

_____

_____

_____

Chapter 3

_____

_____

_____

_____

Chapter 4

_____

_____

_____

_____

Chapter Summarization

Chapter 7

_____

_____

_____

_____

Chapter 21

_____

_____

_____

_____

Chapter 29

_____

_____

_____

_____

Comprehension Questions

1. In chapter one Augustine is very critical of those who attach Christianity. Give an example of his criticism by quoting one of the lines in chapter one.

2. Augustine provides a three point outline in chapter two of what he is attempting to do in the *City of God*. What are his three points?

3. In chapter three Augustine challenges the critics of Christianity by appealing to what example?

4. In chapter four Augustine again criticizes the gods of his opponents. What is his criticism of the gods in this chapter and why is he so confident in his challenge?

5. In chapter twenty-one Augustine makes a complicated argument to make what point?

6. In chapter twenty-nine Augustine invites his opponents to a Country. Is it a real country? What is Augustine inviting them to join?

7. In chapter twenty-nine Augustine accuses his opponents of not wanting a peaceful life, but rather desiring something else – what does Augustine say they really desire?

Vocabulary

If man's sickly understanding would not set plain truth at defiance, but humbly submit this common infirmity to the tonic of wholesome doctrine until, by **filial** trust in God's help, it regained its strength, those who think straight and express their thoughts in well-chosen speech would have no need of many words to correct the errors of baseless assumption.

Chapter 1, ¶ 1, line 3

It may be an excess of blindness which prevents them from seeing the most glaring facts, or a perverse **obstinacy** which prevents them from accepting the facts when seen.

Chapter 1, ¶ 1, line 12

For, those who cannot grasp what is said, or, if they understand the truth, are too **obdurate** to accept it, keep on replying and, according to Holy Writ, 'speak iniquity' and never weary of empty words.

Chapter 1, ¶ 2, line 4

These **calumniators**, I pointed out, are wicked, impious, and degenerate descendants – not to say, the worst enemies – of those sturdier Romans whose many noble deeds are on the lips of men and live in the pages of history.

Chapter 2, ¶ 3, line 4

Why, then, did the gods permit the misfortunes I shall mention to fall on their devotees before the **promulgation** of Christ's teaching provoked their wrath and proscribed their sacrifices?

Chapter 3, ¶ 2, line 11

Cicero lets that same Scipio who had destroyed Carthage voice his opinion of the state at a time when men felt a **presentiment** that it would soon be brought low by the rottenness which Sallust describes.

Chapter 21, ¶ 1, line 9

Let its **panegyrists** really take a look at the republic in the day of those ancient men and customs.

Chapter 21, ¶ 11, line 1

There are many confirmatory opinions expressed in that discussion both by himself and by the **interlocutors** he introduced.

Chapter 21, ¶ 12, line 8

Give no heed to the degenerate **progeny** who blame Christ and Christians for what they call bad times, and long for times which assure them, not a peaceful life, but undisturbed wickedness.

Chapter 29, ¶ 3, line 1

Vocabulary – Write the vocabulary word on the first line (a help for spelling) followed by the definition.

1. **Filial**

   _____. _____

   _____.

2. **Obstinacy**

   _____. _____

   _____.

3. **Obdurate**

   _____. _____

   _____.

4. **Calumniators**

   _____. _____

   _____.

5. **Promulgation**

   _____. _____

   _____.

6. **Presentiment**

   _____. _____

   _____.

7. **Panegyrists**

   _____. _____

   _____.

8. **Interlocutors**

   _____. _____

   _____.

9. **Progeny**

   _____. _____

   _____.

Memorable Quote

Our own generation inherited the republic, an exquisite masterpiece, indeed, though faded with age; but it failed to restore its original colors. Worse, alas; it did not even move a finger to preserve as much as its form, or its barest outlines.

- Chapter 21 ¶ 7, page 7

Focus Passages

Book III, Chapter 1 (page 78) –

It seems to me I have already said enough about the evils which work havoc on men's souls and morals, and which they must shun at all costs. I have shown that, far from having done aught to save their worshipers from the miseries that lay heavy upon them, the false gods did their utmost to increase the burden beyond endurance.

I must now turn to those calamities which are the only things our accusers have no wish to endure. Such are hunger, disease, war, plunder, imprisonment, massacre, and horrors such as I have mentioned in Book I. Though these do not make men evil, evildoers regard them as the only evil. Yet, they feel no shame that they themselves are evil amid the things they praise as good. They are more pained if their villa is poor than if their life is bad, as though man's greatest good were to have everything good except himself.

The fact is that the gods did not ward off the evils which pagans dread, even at a time when they were freely worshiped. At various times and in different places before the coming of our Redeemer, calamities beyond counting and description were scourging mankind. Yet, what others besides your recreant gods did the world worship? I except, of course, the Hebrew nation, and a few individuals beyond its pale, wherever by God's grace and His secret and righteous judgment they were found worthy.

Book III, Chapter 4 (page 81) –

Someone may say to me: 'Do you believe all that stuff?" My answer is that I do not. Even one of the most learned pagans, Varro, if not with outright decisiveness and confidence, still cautiously avows that all this is sheer nonsense. For all that, he affirms that it is expedient for states that men of valor should claim divine lineage, however shallow the pretence. This is on the theory that, by that sublime fiction, the human spirit, urged on by the self-assurance of being divinely born, will venture into great exploits and, by the confidence such illusion inspires, achieve more signal success.

You cannot but observe how wide a door this view, which I have summarized in my own words, would open to sham and false pretense. This is especially so where lies even about the gods are regarded as advantageous to the people. Endless fictions will be invented, and invested with a so-called sacred and religious character.

Book III, Chapter 31 (page 82) –

Let the pagans blame their own gods for all their woes, instead of repaying our Christ with ingratitude for all His good gifts. Certain it is that, when calamities rained upon them, 'the altars streamed with Sabaean incense and were fresh with fragrance of chaplets.' While Romans were shedding Roman blood, not only in ordinary places, but before the very altars of the gods, the pagan priesthood was held in honor, the shrines were bright, all was sacrifices, play and orgies in the temples. Note that Cicero sought no temple for sanctuary, because that had been of no avail for Mucius. But, the pagans of our day, while they have far less reason to decry the era, have either fled for sanctuary to the most hallowed Christian places, or have been taken there by the barbarians to save their lives.

I need not repeat what I have already said or mention anything I had to omit, but one thing is certain, and anyone whose mind is free from bias will readily admit it: If mankind had embraced Christ's teaching before the Punic Wars, and if there had followed the terrible devastation of those wars in Europe and Africa, there is not one of those intolerable critics who would not have blamed those evils on the Christian religion.

Their outcries would have been even more intolerable, especially in what touches the Romans, if the invasion of the Gauls, or the inundation of the Tiber and the devastating fires, or, what was words, the horrors of those civil wars of evil memory had occurred after the acceptance and spread of Christianity…Against what other people but Christians would they have been charged as crimes?

Chapter Summarization

Chapter 1

_____

_____

_____

_____

Chapter 2

_____

_____

_____

Chapter 3

_____

_____

_____

Chapter 4

_____

_____

_____

Chapter Summarization

Chapter 31

_____

_____

_____

_____

Comprehension Questions

1. In chapter one, Augustine says instead of saving their worshipers from misery, the pagan gods have instead done what to their followers?

2. By saying this, is Augustine acknowledging that other gods actually exist? Explain.

3. Augustine goes on in chapter one to charge that the pagan gods failed to do what? How does he make his point?

4. In chapter two Augustine ridicules Neptune and Apollo for being unable to predict that Laomedon was going to cheat them of their pay. Because such gods are so undependable Augustine poses a question to their followers – what is the question?

5. It is clear that, in Augustine's opinion, it is foolish to believe in the pagan gods. In chapter four Augustine uses one of the most learned of pagans to make this point. How does he use this person as an example and what does this person say is the reason for encouraging people to believe in the pagan gods?

6. Augustine is clearly troubled by the blame given to Christians for the problems of Rome. In chapter thirty-one he says the pagans ought to blame whom?

7. In chapter thirty-nine Augustine goes on to complain that the critics of Christianity want to restore what? He sees this as a foolish endeavor for what reason?

Vocabulary

At various times and in different places before the coming of our Redeemer, **calamities** beyond counting and description were scourging mankind.

Chapter 1, ¶ 3, line 4

Confining myself to Rome alone and to the Roman Empire, that is, to the city itself and to the people linked with it either by alliance or by subjection, I shall speak of the visitations they experienced before the coming of Christ, but after their incorporation into the Roman **body politic**.

Chapter 1, ¶ 4, line7

Homer himself has not given easy **credence** to the fable, for, while on the one hand he represents Neptune battling against the Trojans, on the other he has Apollo fighting for them, in spite of the fact that, as the fable runs, both took offense at the **perjury**.

Chapter 2, ¶ 2, lines 7 and 10

For, as a rule, they are the **perpetrators** and teachers of evil, not its avengers.

Chapter 3, ¶ 1, line 6

Was it because the former was committed in the face of Menelaus' wrath; the latter, with Vulcan's **connivance**?

Chapter 3, ¶ 2, line 5

For all that, he affirms that it is **expedient** for states that men of valor should claim divine lineage, however shallow the **pretence**.

Chapter 4, ¶ 1, lines 5 and 6

This on the theory that, by that **sublime** fiction, the human spirit, urged on by the self-assurance of being divinely born, will venture into great exploits and, by the confidence such illusion inspires, achieve more signal success.

Chapter 4, ¶ 1, line 7

Vocabulary – Write the vocabulary word on the first line (a help for spelling) followed by the definition.

1. Calamities

   _____. _____

   _____.

2. Body politic

   _____. _____

   _____.

3. Credence

   _____. _____

   _____.

4. Perjury

   _____. _____

   _____.

5. Perpetrators

   _____. _____

   _____.

6. Connivance

   _____. _____

   _____.

7. Expedient

   _____. _____

   _____.

8. Pretence

   _____. _____

   _____.

9. Sublime

   _____. _____

   _____.

Memorable Quote

I have shown that, far from having done aught to save their worshipers from the miseries that lay heavy upon them, the false gods did their utmost to increase the burden beyond endurance.

- Chapter 1 ¶ 1, page 78

Focus Passages

Book IV, Chapter 1 (page 84) –

Among our accusers there is an ignorant rabble, incited by the authority of the learned to cast greater odium upon us. These simple souls imagine that the abnormal calamities that have occurred in our own day were entirely unknown in the past. This foolish opinion is encouraged even by those who know it to be false, but who pretend ignorance in order to give an air of truth to their grumblings. Hence, I have gone to the books in which their own historians have recorded, for men's information, the things that happened in the past, and from these I have proved two important facts: first, that the actual events were far different from what these people imagined; second, that the false gods which pagans then worshiped in the open, and now worship under cover, were unclean spirits, malignant and lying demons. The truth of this is clear from the fact that these demons go so far as to take delight in their own villainies, to the extent of wanting them exhibited, either as facts or as fictions, in the festivals celebrated in their honor. I have also pointed out that, as long as these villainies are exhibited for imitation under divine sanction, so to speak, it is impossible to restrain weak humans from actually reproducing in their own lives the abominable acts committed by the gods.

Book IV, Chapter 3 (pages 87-88) –

In order to be perfectly clear on this point, we must not be carried away by hollow verbal blasts and allow our judgment to be confused by the high-sounding words of prattlers about nations, kingdoms, and provinces. Let us imagine two individuals – for each man, like a letter in a word, is an integral part of a city or of a kingdom, however extensive. Of these two men, let us suppose that one is poor, or, better, in moderate circumstances; the other, extremely wealthy. But, our wealthy man is haunted by fear, heavy with cares, feverish with greed, never secure, always restless, breathless from endless quarrels with his enemies. By these miseries, he adds to his possessions beyond measure, but he also piles up for himself a mountain of distressing worries. The man of modest means is content with a small and compact patrimony. He is loved by his own, enjoys the sweetness of peace in his relations with kindred, neighbors, and friends, is religious and pious, of kindly disposition, healthy in body, self-restrained, chaste in morals, and at peace with his conscience.

I wonder if there is anyone so senseless as to hesitate over which of the two to prefer. What is true of these two individuals is likewise true of two families, two nations, two kingdoms; the analogy holds in both cases. If we apply it with care and correct our judgment accordingly, it will be easy to see on which side lies folly and on which true happiness.

Book IV, Chapter 4 (page 88) –

In the absence of justice, what is sovereignty by organized brigandage? For, what are bands of brigands but petty kingdoms?

Book IV, Chapter 28 (pages 97-98) –

Just as the Romans could have had gold money without worshiping the god Aurinus, so they could have had silver and copper money without worshiping either Argentinus or his father Aesculanus. So with the rest, which it would be wearisome for me to repeat. So, also, they could have had their empire, though by no means against the will of the true God. But, if they had ignored and despised that mob of false gods, and, with sincere faith and right living, acknowledged and worshiped that one God alone, they would have won a better kingdom, whether large or small, here below, and, with or without one here, they would have received an eternal one hereafter.

Chapter Summarization

Chapter 1

_____

_____

_____

Chapter 2

_____

_____

_____

Chapter 3

_____

_____

_____

Chapter 4

_____

_____

_____

Chapter Summarization

Chapter 10

_____

_____

_____

_____

Chapter 27

_____

_____

_____

Chapter 28

_____

_____

_____

_____

Comprehension Questions

1. In chapter one, Augustine says *I have also pointed out that, as long as these villainies are exhibited for imitation under divine sanction, so to speak, it is impossible to restrain weak humans from actually reproducing in their own lives the abominable acts committed by the gods.* What warning do you believe he is giving?

2. In chapter two what is the primary reason Augustine gives as to why the pagans are incorrect when they accuse Christianity of being the cause of the problems in the Roman Empire?

3. In chapter three Augustine contrasts a rich man to a poor man. Who does he says has a better life? Do you agree with him? Why?

4. In chapter four Augustine says that one element separates a legitimate kingdom from nothing more than a band of criminals. What is this one element Augustine refers to?

5. In chapter eleven Augustine is attacking as illogical one of the foundations of the religions of Rome. What belief is he attacking?

6. In chapter twenty-seven Augustine says the followers of the Roman gods are being duped. About what are they being misled?

7. In chapter twenty-eight Augustine says the Romans could have worshiped the true God and still gained what?

Vocabulary

Among our accusers there is an ignorant rabble, incited by the authority of the learned to cast great **odium** upon us.

Chapter 1, ¶ 2, line 2

Conflagrations kindled by lightning swallowed up in flames whole regions in the East, while on the coasts of the West waterspouts and floods caused similar devastation.

Chapter 2, ¶ 2, line 14

Let us now consider on what grounds our adversaries affirm that the immensity and long duration of the Roman Empire are gifts of those gods whom, they insist, they have honorably worshiped by the **homage** of infamous plays performed by the ministrations of infamous men.

Chapter 3, ¶1 , line 4

It is still human blood, in men perpetually haunted by the gloomy **spectre** of fear and driven by murderous passions.

Chapter 3, ¶ 1, line 12

In order to be perfectly clear on this point, we must not be carried away by hollow verbal blasts and allow our judgment to be confused by the high-sounding words of **prattlers** about nations, kingdoms, and provinces.

Chapter 3, ¶ 2, line 3

The man of modest means is content with a small and compact **patrimony**.

Chapter 3, ¶ 2, line 14

For, what are bands of **brigands** but petty kingdoms?

Chapter 4, ¶ 1, line 2

If things were as they imagine, their ancient sages should have **postulated** three constituent elements of the world, not four, so that each of the elements might be assigned to each pair of divinities.

Chapter 10, ¶ 2, line 3

We are told in the pagan writings that the learned **pontifex** Scaevola distinguished three classes of divinities handed down to us: the first, by the poets; the second, by the philosophers; the third, by the statesmen.

Chapter 27, ¶ 1, line 1

Vocabulary – Write the vocabulary word on the first line (a help for spelling) followed by the definition.

1. Odium

    _____. _____

    _____.

2. Conflagrations

    _____. _____

    _____.

3. Homage

    _____. _____

    _____.

4. Spectre

    _____. _____

    _____.

5. Prattlers

    _____. _____

    _____.

6. Patrimony

    _____. _____

    _____.

7. Brigands

    _____. _____

    _____.

8. Postulated

    _____. _____

    _____.

9. Pontifex

    _____. _____

    _____.

Memorable Quote

Thus, a good man, though a slave, is free; but a wicked man, though a king, is a slave. For he serves, not one man alone, but, what is worse, as many masters as he has vices. For, it is in reference to vice that the Holy Scripture says: 'For by whom a man is overcome, of the same also he is the slave.'

- Chapter 3 ¶ 5, page 88

Focus Passages

Book V, Chapter 16 (pages 112-113) –

The reward of the saints is altogether different. They were men who, while on earth, suffered reproaches for the City of God which is so much hated by the lovers of this world. That City is eternal. There, no one is born because no one dies. There, there reigns that true and perfect happiness which is not a goddess, but a gift of God – toward whose beauty we can but sigh in our pilgrimage on earth, though we hold the pledge of it by faith. In that City, the sun does not 'rise upon the good and bad' for the Sun of Justice cherishes the good alone. There, where the Truth is a treasure shared by all, there is no need to pinch the poor to fill the coffers of the state.

It was, then, not only to reward the Roman heroes with human glory that the Roman Empire spread. It had a purpose for the citizens of the Eternal City during their pilgrimage on earth. Meditating long and seriously on those great examples, they could understand what love of their Heavenly Fatherland should be inspired by everlasting life, since a fatherland on earth has been so much loved by citizens inspired by human glory.

Book V, Chapter 17 (page 114) –

So far as I can see, it makes no difference at all to political security or public order to maintain the purely human distinction between conquerors and conquered peoples. It adds nothing to the state but empty pomp – fit reward for those who wage fierce battles out of lust for human glory. Do not the Romans pay taxes for their lands as others do? Are they more free to learn than others are? Are there not many Senators in foreign lands who do not even know what Rome looks like? When all the boasting is over, what is any man but just another man? And, even though a crooked world came to admit that men should be honored only according to merit, even human honor would be of no great value. It is smoke that weighs nothing.

Yet, in this matter, too, let us turn to our profit the goodness of God, our Lord. Let us reflect what good things they despised, what suffering they sustained, what passions they subdued for human glory – the sole reward such marvelous virtues merited. Let it help us to suppress our pride when we think of the difference between their city and ours and to reflect how little we can claim to have done if, to gain our City, we do a little good or endure certain ills, when they have done and suffered so much for the sake of the earthly city which is already theirs. Our City is as different from theirs as heaven from earth, as everlasting life from passing pleasure, as solid glory from empty praise, as the company of angels from the companionship of mortals, as the Light of Him who made the sun and moon is brighter than the light of sun and moon. We can learn from this, too, that the remission of sins which makes us citizens of the Eternal City was faintly adumbrated when Romulus gathered the first citizens of his city by providing a sanctuary and immunity for a multitude of criminals.

Book V, Chapter 24 (page 118) –

We call those Christian emperors happy who govern with justice, who are not puffed up by the tongues of flatterers or the services of sychophants, but remember that they are men. We call them happy when they think of sovereignty as a ministry of God and use it for the spread of true religion; when they fear and love and worship God; whey the are in love with the Kingdom in which they need fear no fellow sharers; when they are slow to punish, quick to forgive; when they punish, not out of private revenge, but only when forced by the order and security of the republic, and when they pardon, not to encourage impunity, but with the hope of reform; when they temper with mercy and generosity the inevitable harshness of their decrees.

Chapter Summarization

Chapter 1

_____

_____

_____

_____

Chapter 2

_____

_____

_____

_____

Chapter 9

_____

_____

_____

_____

Chapter 10

_____

_____

_____

_____

Chapter Summarization

Chapter 16

_____

_____

_____

_____

Chapter 17

_____

_____

_____

_____

Chapter 20

_____

_____

_____

_____

Chapter 21

_____

_____

_____

_____

Comprehension Questions

1. In chapter one Augustine rejects what concept as the source of Rome's greatness? What does he claim establishes the kingdoms of men?

2. Augustine discusses two concepts of fate in chapter one. One concept he rejects and the other he accepts. What are the two concepts of fate that he discusses?

3. In chapter nine Augustine uses Cicero in his argument, saying that Cicero claimed God could not do something. What did Cicero claim that God did not have the power to do?

4. At the end of chapter nine Augustine comes to a conclusion. What is his conclusion?

5. Augustine argues in chapter ten that God is omnipotent. Why, in Augustine's opinion, is God omnipotent?

6. At the end of chapter ten Augustine says *no man sins unless it is his choice to sin; and his choice not to sin, that too, God foresaw.* Do you think God's foreknowledge of our choices in any way restricts our free will to make choices?

7. In chapter sixteen Augustine says God rewarded the heroes of Rome with human glory. This reward had a purpose for the citizens of the Eternal City. What was this purpose?

Vocabulary

Surely, though, it is best to say at once what one will have to say as soon as one is asked what is meant by **fate**.
Chapter 1, ¶ 1, line 11

It would be surprising, indeed, if either Posidonius or any other advocate of **sidereal** influence could find any explanation unless he wanted to play on the ignorance of simple minds.
Chapter 2, ¶ 4, line 2

Magnanimous and learned as he was, and with no thought but to save human nature as best he could, Cicero made his choice.
Chapter 9, ¶ 7, line 1

As for the causes which are called **fortuitous** – hence, the name of fortune – we do not say they are unreal.
Chapter 9, ¶ 13, line 1

We say they are **latent**, in the sense that they are hidden in the will either of the true God or one of His spirits.
Chapter 9, ¶13, line 3

We can learn from this, too, that the remission of sins which makes us citizens of the Eternal City was faintly **adumbrated** when Romulus gathered the first citizens of his city by providing a sanctuary and immunity for a multitude of criminals.
Chapter 17, ¶ 3, line 16

The Stoics are right when they say that no picture could be more ugly and **ignominious** and difficult for good people to look at than this.
Chapter 20, ¶ 2, line 4

On another occasion, he let rash **ardor** get the better of him.
Chapter 21, ¶ 4, line 10

We call those Christian emperors happy who govern with justice, who are not puffed up by the tongues of flatterers or the services of **sychophants**, but remember that they are men.
Chapter 24, ¶ 2, line 3

Vocabulary – Write the vocabulary word on the first line (a help for spelling) followed by the definition.

1. Fate

   _____ . _____

   _____ .

2. Sidereal

   _____ . _____

   _____ .

3. Magnanimous

   _____ . _____

   _____ .

4. Fortuitous

   _____ . _____

   _____ .

5. Latent

   _____ . _____

   _____ .

6. Adumbrated

   _____ . _____

   _____ .

7. Ignominious

   _____ . _____

   _____ .

8. Ardor

   _____ . _____

   _____ .

9. Sychophants

   _____ . _____

   _____ .

Memorable Quote

When it is considered how short is the span of human life, does it really matter to a man whose days are numbered what government he must obey, so long as he is not compelled to act against God or his conscience?

- Chapter 17 ¶ 1, page 113

Focus Passage

Book VI, Chapter 6 (pages 130 - 132) –

Marcus Varro, you may be 'the most brilliant' man of your age and 'undoubtedly the most learned.' Still, you are a man, not God. You have not even been raised by the Spirit of God to see truly and to tell freely the nature of the divine. Nevertheless, you see clearly enough to separate what is divine from the silly imaginings of men. Yet, you are afraid to denounce popular opinions which are false, and official traditions which are shams, even though you know in your heart that they are repugnant to what is divine and even to such divinity as our poor human intelligence discerns in the elements of the world. This is clear from you own constant references to these opinions and from the tone of all the writings of your friends.

Your human gifts, however remarkable, do not help you here. In straits like these, human learning, however broad and deep, is of no avail. Your heart is with the God of nature, but your head bows where the state wills. You pour out revenge by openly attacking the gods of mythology but, willy-nilly, what you spill falls on the state divinities, too. You say that the mythical and political gods are at home on the stage and in the cities, while the natural gods are at home in the world. But, your point is that the world was made by God, but theaters and cities by men, and that the same gods who are adored in the temples are derided on the stage, and the same gods to whom sacrifice is offered have plays written in their honor.

It would have been more like a gentleman and a scholar to have divided the gods into those which are natural and those which were introduced by men, and to say of these latter that the account given by the poets differs from that of the priests, but that both accounts are so close in the fellowship of falsehood as to delight the demons whose only battle is with the teaching of truth.

I shall discuss 'natural' theology later; omitting it for the moment, I merely ask: Is anyone willing to ask or hope for eternal life from the mythical gods on the stage or the civic gods in the cosmic shows?

God forbid – may the true God save men from so gross and insane a sacrilege! Just imagine asking eternal life from gods who are pleased and placated by plays which rehearse their own sins. I should think that no one is so irrational and so irreligious as to dance on the edge of such madness. No, neither by mythical nor by political theology does anyone obtain eternal life. The former sows filthy fancies about the gods; the latter reaps by keeping them alive. The one spreads lies, and the other gathers them up; the one belittles divinity with imaginary sins and the other represents this wickedness and calls it public worship; the one puts into song the unmentionable imaginings of men and the other consecrates such things for the festivals of the gods; the one sings sins and crimes and the other loves them; whatever the one discovers or invents the other approves and enjoys.

Both theologies are a disgrace and both should be condemned, but, while the theatrical theology merely teaches turpitude in public, the popular theology wears it like a jewel. Imagine looking for eternal life in places where our brief and passing life is so polluted! If the company of wicked men can so poison our life, once they have won a way into our hearts and minds, what should we say of fellowship with devils who are worshiped by their own wickedness? The truer the wickedness, the worse for the devils; and, the more it is slanderous, the worse for our worship.

I know that some who read what I am writing and are ignorant of things as they are will imagine that only those things in the celebration of such gods are shocking, ridiculous, and unworthy of the divine majesty which are sung by poets and acted on the stage, while the worship of the priests, unlike that of the actors, is pure and free from impropriety. If this were so, no one would ever have thought that dirty plays should be used to honor the gods, and still less would the gods themselves have ordered them to be played. The fact is that no one is ashamed to worship the gods by such plays in the theaters, because the very same things take place in the temples.

Chapter Summarization

Chapter 1

_____

_____

_____

_____

Chapter 2

_____

_____

_____

_____

Chapter 4

_____

_____

_____

_____

Chapter 5

_____

_____

_____

_____

Chapter Summarization

Chapter 6

_____

_____

_____

_____

Chapter 12

_____

_____

_____

_____

Comprehension Questions

1. In chapter one Augustine argues that it is impossible for one to receive what from the pagan gods?

2. In chapter two Augustine says that while the great scholar Marcus Varro worshipped the pagan gods he was fearful about what? What led to his fear?

3. In chapter four Augustine criticizes Varro for the order in which he discusses human things and divine things. What does Augustine say this signifies about what Varro believes about religion? What does Augustine believe this proves about Varro's entire belief system?

4. Augustine discusses three types of theology in chapter five. Name these three types of theology and discuss what he means by each type.

5. Chapter six is a powerful and strident critique of Varro's religious philosophy. List three examples of Augustine's blistering attack on Varro.

6. Do you believe that Augustine should have been more civil in his criticism of his opponents? Why or why not?

7. In chapter seven Augustine defines what he means by eternal life. What is his definition?

Vocabulary

But, what of those men, some of them extremely learned and acute, who boast of having written useful books of instructions to help people to know why each of the different gods is to be prayed to, and what is to be asked of each, and how to avoid the unbecoming **absurdity** of asking, like a clown on a stage, for water from Bacchus or for wine from the Lymphae?

Chapter 1, ¶ 4, line 8

Here they are so assigned to such tiny and fragmentary **adjuncts** of our sad and transient life that, when you ask one of them for something in the department of another, you get a situation as ridiculous as a **scurrilous** embarrassment on the stage.

Chapter 1, ¶ 5, lines 9 and 11

Yet, the fact is that he has set forth things for the whole world to read which are **abhorrent** to philosophers and fools and are of no service at all to true religion.

Chapter 2, ¶ 4, line 11

It looks very much as though, for all his **acumen** and learning, he had none of that liberty of spirit which is a gift of the Holy Spirit, and was, in fact, a slave to legalism, and tradition; yet, below his superficial commendation of pagan religion, there is a hint of his real convictions in some of his admissions.

Chapter 2, ¶ 4, line 13

Here he could speak boldly and with **impunity** – and he did so without a shadow of **ambiguity** – of the wrong done to divinity by laying fables.

Chapter 5, ¶ 2, lines 1 and 2

Both theologies are a disgrace and both should be condemned, but, while the theatrical theology merely teaches **turpitude** in public, the popular theology wears it like a jewel.

Chapter 6, ¶ 6, line 3

I know that some who read what I am writing and are ignorant of things as they are will imagine that only those things in the celebration of such gods are shocking, ridiculous, and unworthy of the divine majesty which are sung by poets and acted on the stage, while the worship of the priests, unlike that of the actors, is pure and free from **impropriety**.

Chapter 6, ¶ 7, line 6

Vocabulary – Write the vocabulary word on the first line (a help for spelling) followed by the definition.

1. **Absurdity**

   —————————— . ——————————————————————————————

   ——— .

2. **Adjuncts**

   —————————— . ——————————————————————————————

   ——— .

3. **Scurrilous**

   —————————— . ——————————————————————————————

   ——— .

4. **Abhorrent**

   —————————— . ——————————————————————————————

   ——— .

5. **Acumen**

   —————————— . ——————————————————————————————

   ——— .

6. **Impunity**

   —————————— . ——————————————————————————————

   ——— .

7. **Ambiguity**

   —————————— . ——————————————————————————————

   ——— .

8. **Turpitude**

   —————————— . ——————————————————————————————

   ——— .

9. **Impropriety**

   —————————— . ——————————————————————————————

   ——— .

Memorable Quote

It does not at once follow that what belongs to a city can belong to the world, although cities are part of the world. For, it can happen that in a city, by reason of false opinions, things can be believed or worshiped which have no real existence either in the world or outside of it.

- Chapter 5 ¶ 7, page 130

Focus Passage

Book VII, Preface (page 135) –

The issue at stake is very great. What I want to bring out is that, although we depend on the true and truly holy Divinity for such things as are needed to support our weakness in this present life, nevertheless, we should not seek and worship God for the sake of the passing cloud of this mortal life, but for the sake of that happy life which cannot be other than everlasting.

Book VII, Chapter 30 (page 140) –

The God we worship chose certain spirits and gave them the power of foresight, and through them He makes prophecies. To others He gave the gift of healing. He controls the beginnings, progress, and endings of wars, when they are needed for the punishment or reformation of mankind. He rules the universal element of fire, so vehement and violent, yet so necessary for the equilibrium of nature. He is the Creator and Ruler of all the water of the universe. He made the sun, the brightest of all luminous bodies, and He gave it an appropriate energy and motion.

Book VII, Chapter 30 (page 141) –

Yet, the Creator of every nature has so ordained that each of His creatures is permitted to have and to exercise powers of its own. Although without Him they could not exist, their essence is different from His. He does many things by the ministry of angels, but their only source of beatitude is God Himself. And He Himself, and not the angels, is the source of men's beatitude, even though He sometimes uses angels as messengers to men. It is from this one true God that we look for everlasting life.

Book VII, Chapter 31 (page 141) –

I have already said something of the general blessings of God, which, in the natural course of things, come to the good and the bad alike. However, beyond this bounty, He has reserved for the good a special sign of His great love. We can never sufficiently thank Him for the gifts of nature: that we exist and are alive, that we can enjoy the sight of earth and sky, that we have a reasoning mind by which we can seek Him who has made all these things. Yet, for the greater gifts of grace there are not hearts enough or tongues enough in all the world even to try to thank Him. For, when we were burdened and broken by our sins, and our minds were turned from His light and blinded by the love of the darkness of iniquity, He did not leave us to ourselves, but sent to us His Word, who is His only Son, so that, by His birth and passion in the flesh He assumed for our salvation, we might learn how highly God esteemed our human nature, and that we might by cleansed from all our sins by His unique Sacrifice and, by His Spirit, have Love poured into our hearts, so that, with all our warring over, we might come to everlasting rest in the supreme blessedness of gazing on His face.

Book VII, Chapter 33 (page 142) –

It was by no means of the true religion alone that it could be made manifest that the gods of the pagans were nothing but unclean spirits who used the memory of people departed or the images of earthly creatures to get themselves reckoned as gods and who then rejoiced with proud impurity that divine honors should be paid to such disgusting and indecent things, all the while hating to see men's souls turn to the true God. From their horrible and hateful domination a man is delivered by faith in Him who showed us the way to rise by going to a depth of humility as great as the height of pride from which they fell.

Chapter Summarization

Chapter 5

_____

_____

_____

_____

Chapter 6

_____

_____

_____

_____

Chapter 7

_____

_____

_____

_____

Chapter 30

_____

_____

_____

_____

Chapter Summarization

Chapter 31

_____

_____

_____

_____

Chapter 32

_____

_____

_____

_____

Chapter 33

_____

_____

_____

_____

Comprehension Questions

1. 1. In chapter five Augustine says Varro believes the true gods are what?

2. In chapter six Augustine says that Marcus Varro believes that God is the soul of the universe or cosmos. In this way, Varro seems to indicate there is but one God, but Varro must find a way to prove there are really many gods. How, according to Augustine, does Varro accomplish this?

3. In chapter seven Augustine tells us that Varro believes that the god Janus is the cosmos. If this is true, says Augustine, Varro does not need to talk about the existence of what?

4. In chapter thirty Augustine says we look for what from the one true God?

5. In chapter thirty-one Augustine says we can never thank God enough for what?

6. In chapter thirty-two Augustine says that eternal life has been announced to all. By whom was it announced and what were the methods used?

7. In chapter thirty-three Augustine says the pagan gods were chosen more for the _____ than for the nobility of their _____.

Vocabulary

But, surely, we must appeal from the intelligence of Varro, intoxicated by esotericism, to the sober **prudence** of his ordinary insight, as when he admits, first, that those who first set up images of the gods for the people 'took away their fear but added to their error,' and, second, that the ancient Romans had a purer reverence for the gods when they had no images.

Chapter 5, ¶ 2, line 2

For, likely enough, if the early Romans had worshiped images, Varro would have been too afraid to mention the feelings against setting up images – true as that fact was – and his account of the dangerous and empty figments of this **esoteric** doctrine would have been more lengthy and lofty than ever.

Chapter 5, ¶ 2, line 12

And, if natural theology is not true, then the political is of still less value and even falser, since it deals more with merely **corporeal** natures.

Chapter 5, ¶ 4, line 19

From the highest circle of the heavens down to the circle of the moon, the planets, and stars are **ethereal** souls.

Chapter 6, ¶ 3, line 2

Between the circle of the moon and that of the highest cloud and the winds, the soul is **aerial**, and it can be seen with the mind only, not with the eyes.

Chapter 6, ¶ 3, line 5

We adore God who made heaven and earth and all that they contain, God who made every kind of soul, from the lowest that lives without sensation and intellection through the **sentient** up to the soul that can think.

Chapter 29, ¶ 1, line 12

He made the sun, the brightest of all **luminous** bodies, and He gave it an appropriate energy and motion.

Chapter 30, ¶ 2, line 9

The truth is that all these actions and energies belong to the one true God, who is really a God, who is wholly present everywhere, is confined by no frontiers and bound by no hindrances, is indivisible and **immutable**, and, though His nature has no need of either heaven or of earth, He fills them both with His presence and His power.

Chapter 30, ¶ 4, line 8

The best that can be said of Varro's interpretations or of any interpretations of this sort is that, although they have nothing to do with the true God and with the eternal life which is the very purpose of religion, they do help to **mitigate** the offense given by the mysteries, by suggesting that some ill-understood indecency or absurdity becomes clear in the light of some correlative phenomena in nature.

Chapter 33, ¶ 3, line 4

Vocabulary – Write the vocabulary word on the first line (a help for spelling) followed by the definition.

1. **Prudence**

   _____. _____

   _____.

2. **Esoteric**

   _____. _____

   _____.

3. **Corporeal**

   _____. _____

   _____.

4. **Ethereal**

   _____. _____

   _____.

5. **Aerial**

   _____. _____

   _____.

6. **Sentient**

   _____. _____

   _____.

7. **Luminous**

   _____. _____

   _____.

8. **Immutable**

   _____. _____

   _____.

9. **Mitigate**

   _____. _____

   _____.

Memorable Quote

Yet, for the greater gifts of grace there are not hearts enough or tongues enough in all the world even to try to thank Him.

- Chapter 31 ¶ 1, page 141

Focus Passage

Book VIII, Chapter 6 (page 153) –

From this it follows that neither the whole universe, with its frame, figures, qualities and ordered movement, all the elements and bodies arranged in the heavens and on earth, nor any life – whether merely nourishing and preserving as in trees, or both vegetative and sensitive as in animals, or which is also intellectual as in man, or which needs no nourishment but merely preserves, feels and knows as in angels – can have existence apart from Him whose existence is simple and indivisible. For, in God, being is not one thing and living another – as though He could be and not be living. Nor in God is it one thing to live and another to understand – as though He could live without understanding. Nor in Him is it one thing to know and another to be blessed – as though He could know and not be blessed. For, in God, to live, to know, to be blessed is one and the same as to be.

Book VIII, Chapter 23 (pages 167-168) –

Much of what Hermes says about the one true God, Creator of the world, contains an element of truth, and I cannot understand by what blindness of heart he could wish men to be always subject to gods made, as he admits, by men and how he could deplore the future disappearance of these idols. For, what could be more hapless than a man controlled by his own creations? It is surely easier for a man to cease to be a man by worshiping man-made gods than for idols to become divine by being adored. For it is easier to compare a man to cattle if, for all his human dignity, he lacks understanding than to prefer a work of man to a creation of God, made to His own image – that is, to man himself. It is right, therefore, to reckon a man a recreant to his Creator when he hands himself over to a creation of his own hands.

Book VIII, Chapter 27 (pages 169-170) –

Nevertheless, we do not construct shrines, consecrate priests and render rites and sacrifices for these martyrs. The simple reason is that it is not they but God who is our God. It is true that we honor their shrines because they were holy men of God who fought for truth, even unto death, so that true religion might be made known and falsehoods and fictions be overcome. Others before them who knew the truth were too afraid to express their convictions.

Certainly, no Christian ever heard a priest, standing before an altar built for the honor and service of God over the holy body of a martyr, say in his prayers: "I offer this Sacrifice to thee, Peter, or Paul, or Cyprian." No! Before the monuments of these martyrs, the Sacrifice is offered to God alone, who made them first men and then martyrs and finally associated them with His holy angels in heavenly honor. In celebrating this Sacrifice we thank this true God for their victories and, while renewing our memory of them and calling on God to help us, we encourage ourselves to imitate them in seeking like crowns and palms.

Thus, any signs of veneration paid by pious people at the tombs of martyrs are mere tributes to their memory, not sacred ceremonies nor sacrifices offered to the dead, as to gods. This is true, even of the custom of bringing food to these places – something, by the way, which is not done by more enlightened Christians and in most countries is entirely unknown. However, those who do it bring their food to the tombs and pray that it be sanctified by the merits of the martyrs in the name of the Lord of martyrs. Afterwards, they carry it away, either to eat it themselves or to distribute it to the needy. Anyone who knows that there is only one Sacrifice offered by Christians, here or elsewhere, knows that this custom is not a sacrifice to the martyrs.

Chapter Summarization

Chapter One

_____

_____

_____

Chapter Two

_____

_____

_____

Chapter Three

_____

_____

_____

Chapter Four

_____

_____

_____

Chapter Summarization

Chapter Five

_____

_____

_____

_____

Chapter Six

_____

_____

_____

Chapter Seven

_____

_____

_____

Chapter Eight

_____

_____

_____

_____

Chapter Summarization

Chapter Nine

_____

_____

_____

Chapter Ten

_____

_____

_____

Chapter Eleven

_____

_____

_____

Chapter Twelve

_____

_____

_____

Chapter Summarization

Chapter Thirteen

_____

_____

_____

_____

Chapter Fourteen

_____

_____

_____

Chapter Twenty-Three

_____

_____

_____

Chapter Twenty-Seven

_____

_____

_____

Comprehension Questions

1. In chapter four Augustine discusses the division of Plato's philosophy. What are these divisions and what does each represent?

2. In chapter five Augustine says that Plato is superior to all the other philosophers. What is his reasoning for making this claim?

3. Discuss the meaning of the highest good as described by Augustine in chapter eight. What was the highest good for Plato?

4. Discuss the threefold division mentioned by Augustine in chapter fourteen.

5. In chapter twenty-three Augustine describes Hermes' belief that men can create gods. How is this possible?

6. In chapter twenty-three Augustine says *For, what could be more hapless than a man controlled by his own creations?* What do you think he means by this question?

7. In chapter twenty-seven Augustine discusses the difference between Christians honoring their martyrs and the pagans worshipping their gods and the dead. Explain this difference.

Vocabulary

Before his time, any person of outstanding achievement was called a **sage**.

Chapter 2, ¶ 1, line 8

The fact is, they do not denote what he tries to **insinuate**.

Chapter 5, ¶ 2, line 4

Convinced that no **mutable** reality could be the Most High, they transcended every soul and spirit subject to change in their search for God.

Chapter 6, ¶ 1, line 5

For all their passion for **adroitness** in disputation or, as they would say, dialectics, even this was reckoned a matter of sense perception.

Chapter 7, ¶ 1, line 7

While he cannot endure to have the divinities defamed, they demand that falsely **imputed** depravities be enacted in their honor!

Chapter 13, ¶ 3, line 3

As the Lord and Father has fashioned eternal gods to be like himself, so man has modeled his own deities according to the likeness of his own **countenance**.

Chapter 23, ¶ 3, line 11

For, what could be more **hapless** than a man controlled by his own creations?

Chapter 23, ¶ 7, lines 6

It is right, therefore, to reckon a man a **recreant** to his Creator when he hands himself over to a creation of his own hands.

Chapter 23, ¶ 7, line 13

If, then, we do not ordain priests for the purpose of offering sacrifices to our martyrs, for that would be **incongruous**, improper, and unlawful, since worship is due to God alone, still less do we regale our martyrs with their crimes or with disgraceful plays as the pagans do when they commemorate the sins of their gods – either real sins committed by their deities when they were men or, if their gods were never human, fabricated for the delight of wicked demons.

Chapter 27, ¶ 5, line 2

Vocabulary – Write the vocabulary word on the first line (a help for spelling) followed by the definition.

1. Sage

_____. _____

_____.

2. Insinuate

_____. _____

_____.

3. Mutable

_____. _____

_____.

4. Adroitness

_____. _____

_____.

5. Imputed

_____. _____

_____.

6. Countenance

_____. _____

_____.

7. Hapless

_____. _____

_____.

8. Recreant

_____. _____

_____.

9. Incongruous

_____. _____

_____.

Memorable Quote

For what could be more hapless than a man controlled by his own creations?

- Chapter 23 ¶ 7, page 167

Focus Passage

Book IX, Chapter 2, (page 173) –

For, no one should think it was his duty to gain the friendship of supposedly good demons in order to become through their mediation more acceptable to the gods (all of them good) so that, after death, he may enjoy their society. The danger for such a man is that, deceived by the wiles of malignant spirits and caught in their trap, he may never reach the true God, with whom and in whom and by whom alone the rational, intellectual, and human soul can attain its blessedness.

Book IX, Chapter 3 (page 174) –

Wise men do not yield to passion whey they are tempted either to approve or to perpetuate any action that runs counter to the way of wisdom and the law of justice.

Book IX, Chapter 4 (page 177) –

When the Stoics insist that such things must not be called goods but advantages, this is a fight over words, not an insight into things. What difference does it make whether a Stoic calls a thing good or an advantage if he fears to lose it with the same trembling and pallor as a Peripatetic? A difference in name; the emotions are the same. In reality, if they were faced with the choice of losing these 'goods' or 'advantages' or of committing some sin or crime to save them, both would prefer to give up what is necessary for bodily safety and security rather than give in to a violation of justice.

Even though passions may disturb the inferior part of the soul, a mind thus firmly convinced never permits passion to prevail over rational resolve. On the contrary, the mind is the master and, by refusing consent and by positive resistance, it maintains the sovereignity of virtue. Such a man, as Virgil describes him, was Aeneas:

> 'With mind unmoved he doth remain,
> While tender tears run down in vain.'

Book IX, Chapter 5 (page 178) –

At present, there is no need to develop at length and in detail the doctrine contained in Sacred Scripture – fount of Christian faith – concerning passions, namely, that the mind is subject to God to be ruled and aided while the passions are subject to the mind to be tempered, tamed, and turned to the uses of righteousness. For us the important question is not whether a religious soul is subject to anger, but why this is so; not the fact of sadness, but the source of sadness; not whether a man fears, but what he fears. I hope that no one with common sense will find fault with being angry with a sinner to correct him, being sad with a sufferer to relieve him, being afraid lest a man in danger die. The Stoics, it is true, are accustomed to condemn even compassion; but how much better our Stoic would have been if he had been more moved with compassion for a man in peril than afraid of his own shipwreck.

Book IX, Chapter 5 (page 179) –

However, we may well ask the further question whether our liability to passion even in the performance of duty is not a part of the infirmity of our present life.

Book IX, Chapter 9 (page 181) –

Their (the demons) body should still be considered, not as an eternal chariot for their triumph, but as an eternal chain for their damnation.

Chapter Summarization

Chapter One

_____

_____

_____

_____

Chapter Two

_____

_____

_____

Chapter Three

_____

_____

_____

Chapter Four

_____

_____

_____

_____

Chapter Summarization

Chapter Five

_____

_____

_____

_____

Chapter Six

_____

_____

_____

_____

Chapter Nine

_____

_____

_____

_____

Chapter Twenty-Two

_____

_____

_____

_____

Chapter Summarization

Chapter Twenty-Three

Comprehension Questions

1. In chapter one Augustine addresses the question of whether or not the demons could serve as mediators between men and gods. What is his conclusion? Why does he believe this?

2. In chapter two Augustine says many believe that among the demons there are both good and wicked spirits. Why does he say it is wrong to believe a person should attempt to gain the friendship of any good demons that exist?

3. What is the difference between men and demons, as suggested by Augustine in chapter three?

4. In chapter four Augustine says there is one thing that keeps passion from prevailing. What is it that prevails over passion?

5. In chapter six Augustine says the mind of a demon is a slave to what?

6. In chapter twenty-two Augustine says the angels, as opposed to the demons, have no interest in material an temporal realities (i.e., the things of this world). Why is this?

7. In chapter twenty-three Augustine engages in a conversation about whether or not it is proper to use, as do some, the word "demon" to instead of the word "god." Why is this so troublesome to Augustine?

Vocabulary

In the preceding Book, I raised the question whether demons could possibly mediate, as neighbors and favorites, between the good gods and good men, considering that demons delight in doings that good and wise men are obliged to detest and condemn, as, for example, encouraging sacrilegious fables in which poets impute monstrous immoralities not to this or that man but to the very gods; not to mention the **culpable** and criminal violence of magical arts.

Chapter 1, ¶ 4, line 8

The danger for such a man is that, deceived by the **wiles** of malignant spirits and caught in their trap, he may never reach the true God, with whom and in whom and by whom alone the rational, intellectual, and human soul can attain its blessedness.

Chapter 2, ¶ 2, line 9

Thus, they are not to be compared to those philosophers who, in spite of the inescapable weakness of human nature and the painful **vicissitudes** of life, fact the perturbations of passion with an **imperturbable** mind.

Chapter 3, ¶ 3, lines 7 – 9

For if, under the assaults of these emotions, their minds remained free and masters of the situation, Apuleius could not say that their hearts and minds, like those of men, are tossed on all the surge and tide of passionate **disquietude**.

Chapter 6, ¶ 1, line 8

Now, what kind of mediators between men and gods are these demons through whom men may **circuitously** win the favor of the deities?

Chapter 9, ¶ 1, line 2

For what wickedness or punishment have these false and **fallacious** mediators been hung, as it were, upside down, so that their lower part, the body, unites them with beings above them, and their higher part, the soul, links with beings below them?

Chapter 9, ¶ 2, line 2

And if they admit that, though blessed, they are so not **intrinsically** buy only by their union with God by whom they were created, then they are saying what we say, whatever the name they may give to the angels.

Chapter 23, ¶ 1, line 6

They are so on fire with a holy love of God's beauty, so spiritual, unchangeable, and **ineffable**, that they hold in disdain all things – including themselves – which are less than divine, so that, with every grace that makes them good, they may rejoice in the Giver of all goodness, God.

Chapter 22, ¶ 1, line 6

Vocabulary – Write the vocabulary word on the first line (a help for spelling) followed by the definition.

1. **Culpable**

   _____ . _____

   _____ .

2. **Wiles**

   _____ . _____

   _____ .

3. **Vicissitudes**

   _____ . _____

   _____ .

4. **Imperturbable**

   _____ . _____

   _____ .

5. **Disquietude**

   _____ . _____

   _____ .

6. **Circuitously**

   _____ . _____

   _____ .

7. **Fallacious**

   _____ . _____

   _____ .

8. **Ineffable**

   _____ . _____

   _____ .

9. **Intrinsically**

   _____ . _____

   _____ .

Memorable Quote

Even though passions may disturb the inferior part of the soul, a mind thus firmly convinced never permits passion to prevail over rational resolve.

- Chapter 4 ¶ 9, page 177

Focus Passages

Book X, Chapter 1, (page 189) –

Therefore, whoever they are, these immortal and blessed beings who dwell in heaven, if they do not love us and desire us to be happy, then, undoubtedly, we owe them no service; but, if they love us and desire our happiness, then, indeed, they will wish our happiness to flow from the same source as theirs. For, how could our happiness have any other source than theirs?

Book X, Chapter 3, (pages 190 – 191)

Both in outward signs and inner devotion, we owe to Him that service which the Greeks call *latreía*. Indeed, all of us together, and each one in particular, constitute His temple because He deigns to take for a dwelling both the community of all and the person of each individual. Nor is He greater in all than in each, since He cannot be extended by numbers nor diminished by being shared. When raised to Him, our heart becomes His altar; His only Son is the priest who wins for us His favor. It is only by the shedding of our blood in fighting for His truth that we offer Him bloody victims. We burn the sweetest incense in His sight when we are aflame with holy piety and love. As the best gifts we consecrate and surrender to Him our very selves which He has given us. We dedicate and consecrate to Him the memory of His bounties by establishing appointed days as solemn feats, lest, by the lapse of time, ingratitude and forgetfulness should steal upon us. On the altar of our heart, we offer to Him a sacrifice of humility and praise, aglow with the fire of charity.

In order to see Him as, one day, it will be possible to see and to cling to Him, we cleanse ourselves from every stain of sin and evil desire, sanctifying ourselves by His name. For He is the source of our happiness and the very end of all our aspirations.

Book X, Chapter 6, (page 192)

There is, then, a true sacrifice in every work which unites us in a holy communion with God, that is, in every work that is aimed at that final Good in which alone we can be truly blessed. That is why even mercy shown to our fellow men is not a sacrifice unless it is done for God. A sacrifice, even though it is done or offered by man, is something divine – which is what the ancient Latins meant by the word *sacrificium*. For this reason, a man himself who is consecrated in the name of God and vowed to God is a sacrifice, inasmuch as he dies to the world that he may live for God.

Book X, Chapter 6, (page 193)

Since, therefore, true sacrifices are works of mercy done to ourselves or our neighbor and directed to God, and since works of mercy are performed that we may be freed from misery and, thereby, be happy, and since happiness is only to be found in that Good of which it is said: 'But it is good for me to adhere to my God,' it follows that the whole of that redeemed city, that is, the congregation or communion of saints, is offered as a universal sacrifice to God through the High Priest who, 'taking the form of a servant,' offered Himself in His passion for us that we might be the body of so glorious a Head.

Book X, Chapter 32 (page 204)

My next task is to keep the promise made in Book I and, with God's help, to discuss all that seems necessary concerning the origin, progress, and appropriate ends of these two cities which are inextricably intermingled, as I have said, in the concrete reality of history.

Chapter Summarization

Chapter One

_____

_____

_____

_____

Chapter Two

_____

_____

_____

_____

Chapter Three

_____

_____

_____

_____

Chapter Six

_____

_____

_____

_____

Chapter Summarization

Chapter Seven

_____

_____

_____

_____

Chapter Nineteen

_____

_____

_____

Chapter Twenty

_____

_____

_____

Chapter Thirty-One

_____

_____

_____

_____

Chapter Summarization

Chapter Thirty-Two

Comprehension Questions

1. In chapter one Augustine discusses the idea of happiness. What is, to Augustine, the nature of happiness?

2. How does Augustine make the case that any other gods or spirits that exist would desire not to be worshipped?

3. In chapter six, Augustine discussed the nature of a true sacrifice. What it a true sacrifice and to whom is it directed?

4. In chapter 19 Augustine uses two examples of prohibiting sacrifice being made to anyone except God. What are the examples he uses?

5. In chapter 20 Augustine says there is one *supreme and true sacrifice to which all false sacrifices have given place*. What is that sacrifice?

6. In chapter 31 Augustine contrast the Christian and the Platonist view of the soul. Summarize what he says.

7. In chapter 32 Augustine references Porphyry, and mentions this concept of *the liberation of the soul*. What do you think Augustine means by *the liberation of the soul*?

Vocabulary

Hence, when there is a question of the cult of the deity, the word *religio* is **ambiguous**.
Chapter 1, ¶ 8, line 7

This great Platonist, therefore, says that the rational (or, perhaps, better, the intellectual) soul – in which **genus** he includes the souls of those immortal and blessed spirits who are believed to inhabit the celestial dwellings – has no nature above it except that of God who fashioned the universe and created the soul itself, and that these heavenly beings receive their beatitude and their light for the understanding of truth from the same source as we do.
Chapter 2, ¶ 3, line 2

For our goal (or, as the philosophers in their endless disputes have termed it, our end or good) is nothing else than union with Him whose spiritual embrace, if I may so speak, can alone **fecundate** the intellectual soul and fill it with true virtue.
Chapter 3, ¶ 3, line 12

If, then, the body, which is less than the soul and which the soul uses as a servant or a tool, is a sacrifice when it is used well and rightly for the service of God, how much more so is the soul when it offers itself to God so that, aflame in the fire of divine Love, and with the **dross** of worldly desire melted away, it is remolded into the unchangeable form of God and become beautiful in His sight by reason of the bounty of beauty which He has bestowed upon it.
Chapter 6, ¶ 2, line 12

It is from that city on high, where the will of God is the intelligible and **immutable** law, it is, if I may so speak, from that heavenly court where our case is in good hands that the angelic couriers carry down to us the Sacred Scripture, in which it is written: 'He that sacrificeth to gods, shall be put to death, save only to the Lord.'
Chapter 7, ¶ 1, line 13

The spirits, then, who claims divinity for themselves take pleasure not in the fumes of bodies but in the soul of any **suppliant** whom they dominate, once they have deceived and seduced him; and they bar from him the way to the true God, so that, while rendering homage to some being other than God, he is unable to offer himself in sacrifice to Him.
Chapter 19, ¶ 4, line 3

This one sacrifice was **prefigured**, in a variety of ways, as though one idea were being expressed in many words to drive in the truth without boring the reader.
Chapter 20, ¶ 1, line 14

Neither Porphyry nor any other Platonist can discover in our way of salvation the kind of divination and prophecy relating to earthly affairs and mortal life which they discover in soothsaying and magical **prognostications** and rightly despise.
Chapter 32, ¶ 16, line 4

Vocabulary

My next task is to keep the promise made in Book I and, with God's help, to discuss all that seems necessary concerning the origin, progress, and appropriate ends of these two cities which are **<u>inextricably</u>** intermingled, as I have said, in the concrete reality of history.

Chapter 32, ¶ 20, line 13

Vocabulary – Write the vocabulary word on the first line (a help for spelling) followed by the definition.

1. **Ambiguous**

_____. _____

_____.

2. **Genus**

_____. _____

_____.

3. **Fecundate**

_____. _____

_____.

4. **Dross**

_____. _____

_____.

5. **Immutable**

_____. _____

_____.

6. **Suppliant**

_____. _____

_____.

7. **Prefigured**

_____. _____

_____.

8. **Prognostications**

_____. _____

_____.

9. **Inextricably**

_____. _____

_____

Memorable Quote

It is only by the shedding of our blood in fighting for His truth that we offer Him bloody victims.

- Chapter 3 ¶ 2, page 190

Focus Passages

Book XI, Chapter 3, (page 207) –
This Mediator, first through the Prophets, then by His own lips, afterwards through the Apostles, revealed whatever He considered necessary. He also inspired the Scripture, which is regarded as canonical and of supreme authority and to which we give credence concerning all those truths we ought to know and yet, of ourselves, are unable to learn.

Book XI, Chapter 6, (page 211) –
The distinguishing mark between time and eternity is that the former does not exist without some movement and change, while in the latter there is no change at all.

Book XI, Chapter 7, (page 213) –
At any rate, the creature's knowledge in comparison with that of the Creator might be said to be dim as twilight. Yet, it breaks into dawn and brightens to morning when it is employed in the praise and love of God. Nor does the darkness of night ever fall so long as the Creator is not abandoned for love of the creature.

Book XI, Chapter 9, (page 217) –
For, 'the true light that enlightens every man who comes into the world' illumines every pure angel that he may be light not in himself but in God. And, once an angel rejects this Light, he becomes impure. Thus, all those who are called unclean spirits are no longer light in the Lord but darkness in themselves, being deprived of a participation in His eternal light. For, evil has no positive nature; what we call evil is merely the lack of something that is good.

Book XI, Chapter 12, (page 221) –
These saints, however, although certain of their reward if they persevere, can never be sure of their perseverance. For, no man can be sure that he will continue to the end to act and advance in grace unless this fact is revealed to him by God. In His just and secret counsel, God, although He never deceives anyone, gives but few assurances in this matter.

Book XI, Chapter 16, (page 224) –
Thus, a person who evaluates according to reason has far more freedom of choice than one who is driven by want or drawn by passion. For, reason can see the gradation of things in an objective hierarchy of values, while necessity must consider them as means to an end. Reason seeks for what seems true in the light of the intellect, while passion craves for what seems pleasant to the senses.

Book XI, Chapter 21, (page 227) –
Thus, He comprehends all that takes place in time – the not-yet-existing future, the existing present, and the no-longer-existing past – in an immutable and eternal present. He does not see differently with the eyes and the mind, for He is not composed of soul and body. Nor is there any then, now, and afterwards in His knowledge, for, unlike ours, it suffers no change with triple time – present, past, and future. With Him, 'there is no change, nor shadow of alteration.'

Chapter Summarization

Chapter Three

_____

_____

_____

_____

Chapter Six

_____

_____

_____

Chapter Seven

_____

_____

_____

Chapter Eight

_____

_____

_____

Chapter Summarization

Chapter Nine

_____

_____

_____

_____

Chapter Twenty-Two

_____

_____

_____

Chapter Twenty-Six

_____

_____

_____

Comprehension Questions

1. In chapter three Augustine discusses how we know the revealed truth of God. In Augustine's opinion, how has God communicated this truth to humanity?

2. In chapter six Augustine discusses the difference between time and eternity. What is, according to Augustine, the difference?

3. We are familiar with the six days of creation in Genesis. In chapter seven Augustine observes, though, that the first three days of creation take place before the creation of the sun. Without the sun – and the 24 hour day that comes with the sun – how, according to Augustine, do we measure a day?

4. At the end of the six days of creation Genesis tells us that God rested. In chapter eight Augustine describes what this rest means. How does Augustine define the "rest" of God?

5. Augustine spends a good deal of Book XI discussing angels. In chapter nine he discusses when angels were created. At what stage of creation, in Augustine's opinion, were the angels created?

6. In chapter twenty-two Augustine touches on the question of theodicy (the simultaneous existence of a loving God and suffering in the world) when he says "the goodness of creation is the goodness of God." He acknowledges the existence of suffering through things such as fire, cold, wild beasts, etc. How does he answer the charge of the skeptics that these things seem to argue against the goodness of God's creation?

7. In chapter twenty-six Augustine describes something he calls the "trinity of being." What is the trinity of being? More than a millennia later a philosopher would make almost the exact claim in his famous statement *cogito ergo sum*. What is the name of the philosopher and what is the meaning of the phrase *cogito ergo sum*?

Vocabulary

For, quite apart from the voice of the Prophets, the very order, changes, and movements in the universe, the very beauty of form in all that is visible, proclaim, however silently, both that the world was created and also that its Creator could be none other than God whose greatness and beauty are both **ineffable** and invisible.

Chapter 4, ¶ 3, line 11

Because, if they **excogitate** infinite periods of time before the world, in which they cannot see how God could have had nothing to do, they ought to conceive of infinite reaches of space beyond the visible universe.

Chapter 5, ¶ 1, line 7

By 'abyss' is meant a **conglomeration** of earth and water; and, of course, with no light, there is necessarily darkness.

Chapter 9, ¶ 1, line 20

We cannot presume that they shared in wisdom equally with the angels who enjoy a **plentitude** of true happiness precisely because they were never deceived concerning its eternity.

Chapter 11, ¶ 2, line 4

Neither does His attention pass from thought to thought, for His knowledge embraces everything in a single spiritual **contuition**

Chapter 21, ¶ 4, line 3

There is no Creator higher than God, no art more **efficacious** than the Word of God, no better reason why something good should be created than that the God who creates is good.

Chapter 21, ¶ 6, line 1

Without a doubt, they prove with what **alacrity** they would accept immortality – at any rate, one that involved no worse affliction than perpetual **indigence**.

Chapter 27, ¶ 2, lines 8 and 9

For, this is the first number made up of **aliquot** parts, a sixth, a third and a half, respectively, one, two, and three, totaling six.

Vocabulary – Write the vocabulary word on the first line (a help for spelling) followed by the definition.

1. **Ineffable**

   _____ . _____

   _____

2. **Excogitate**

   _____ . _____

   _____

3. **Conglomeration**

   _____ . _____

   _____

4. **Plentitude**

   _____ . _____

   _____

5. **Contuition**

   _____ . _____

   _____

6. **Efficacious**

   _____ . _____

   _____

7. **Alacrity**

   _____ . _____

   _____

8. **Indigence**

   _____ . _____

   _____

9. **Aliquot**

   _____ . _____

   _____

Memorable Quote

For, we do not call a man good because he knows what is good, but because he loves it.

- Chapter 28 ¶ 1, page 238

Focus Passages

Book XII, Chapter 1, (page 245) –

In fact, there is no other good which can make any rational or intellectual creature happy except God. Not every creature has the potentialities for happiness. Beasts, trees, stones, and such things neither acquire nor have the capacity for this gift. However, every creature which has this capacity receives it, not from itself, since it has been created out of nothing, but from its Creator. To possess Him is to be happy; to lose Him is to be in misery. And, of course, that One whose beatitude depends upon Himself as His own good and not on any other good can never be unhappy since He can never lose Himself.

Book XII, Chapter 3, (page 247) –

In Scripture, those who oppose God's rule, not by nature but by sin, are called His enemies. They can do no damage to Him, but only to themselves; their enmity is not a power to harm, but merely a velleity to oppose Him. In any case, God is immutable and completely invulnerable. Hence, the malice by which His so-called enemies oppose God is not a menace to Him, but merely bad for themselves – an evil because what is good in their nature is wounded. It is not their nature, but the wound in their nature, that is opposed to God – as evil is opposed to good.

Book XII, Chapter 3, (pages 247 – 248) –

Just consider the harm done by these wounds – the loss of integrity, of beauty, of health, of virtue, or of any other natural good which can be lost or lessened by sin or sickness. If a nature has nothing of goodness to lose, then there is no harm done by lacking this nothing and, consequently, there is nothing wrong. For there is no such thing as something wrong that does no harm.

Book XII, Chapter 4, (page 249) –

That is why, in those situations where it is beyond our power to understand the providence of God, we are rightly commanded to make an act of faith rather than allow the rashness of human vanity to criticize even a minute detail in the masterpiece of our Creator.

Book XII, Chapter 5, (page 250) –

The conclusion from all this is that God is never to be blamed for any defects that offend us, but should ever be praised for all the perfection we see in the natures He has made. For God is Absolute Being and, therefore, all other being that is relative was made by Him. No being that was made from nothing could be on a par with God, nor could it even be at all, were it not made by Him.

Book XII, Chapter 22, (page 262) –

Therefore, God created one sole individual, not that he was meant to remain alone deprived of human companionship, but in order that the unity of society and the bond of harmony might mean more to man, since men were to be united not only by the likeness of nature but also by the affection of kinship. God did not even wish to create the woman who was to be mated with man in the same way that He created man but, rather, out of him, in order that the whole human race might be derived entirely from one single individual.

Book XII, Chapter 24, (page 263) –

The 'hand' of God means the power of God which works in an invisible way to produce even visible results.

Chapter Summarization

Chapter Five

_____

_____

_____

_____

Chapter Six

_____

_____

_____

_____

Chapter Eight

_____

_____

_____

_____

Chapter Twenty-Three

_____

_____

_____

_____

Chapter Summarization

Chapter Twenty-Four

_____

_____

_____

_____

Chapter Twenty-Six

_____

_____

_____

_____

Chapter Twenty-Eight

_____

_____

_____

_____

Comprehension Questions

1. In chapter five Augustine says that all things are good. Why, in his view, are all things good?

2. In chapter six Augustine discusses the cause of sin in the evil angels. What caused them to sin?

3. In chapter eight Augustine discusses the difference between an efficient cause and in inefficient cause?

4. Augustine says in chapter twenty-three that *God foresaw that a community of saints would be called to supernatural adoption.* To what is he referring?

5. In chapter twenty-four Augustine discusses God's creation of Adam, which he says is done by the *hand of God.* Explain what he means by the *hand of God* in terms of the creation of Adam.

6. What does Augustine mean in chapter twenty-six when he says that the word *form* has two meanings?

7. In chapter twenty-eight Augustine writes *As for that greater governance of divine providence, everything that happens has a purpose even though the causes are hidden.* Augustine seems to be saying that everything that happens is predetermined. Do you believe this?

Vocabulary

Preferring the **pomp** of pride to this sublimity of eternity, the craftiness of vanity to the certainty of truth, and the turmoil of dissension to the union of love, they become proud, deceitful, and envious.

Chapter 1, ¶ 3, line 1

This explanation just given seemed to me necessary to **forestall** the objection that the apostate spirits might have received from some principle other than God a nature different from that of the other angels.

Chapter 2, ¶ 1, line 1

They can do no damage to Him, but only to themselves; their enmity is not a power to harm, but merely a **velleity** to oppose Him.

Chapter 3, ¶ 1, line 4

It is all but impossible to **enumerate** all the good uses to which fire is put throughout the world.

Chapter 4, ¶ 3, line 22

If it existed in some nature, then it **vitiated**, corrupted, injured that nature and, therefore, deprived it of some good.

Chapter 6, ¶ 4, line 2

God was not unaware that man would sin and, being subjected to death, would propagate mortals destined to die; and that these mortals would go so far in the monstrousness of sin that even the beasts without power of rational choice, that had been created in numbers from the waters and the earth, would live more securely and peacefully among their own kind than men – even though the human race had been given a single **progenitor** for the very purpose of promoting harmony.

Chapter 23, ¶ 1, line 8

It was by this same divine creative force, which knows not what it is to be made but only how to make, that roundness was given to the eye, to the apple, and to other objects that are by nature round and which we see all about, taking on their form with no **extrinsic** cause but by the **intrinsic** power of the Creator, who said: 'Do not I fill heaven and earth?'

Chapter 26, ¶ 2, lines 8 and 9

Although it is true that this or that emotion of a pregnant woman may have some effect on the child she is bearing – as Jacob's **variegated** staffs affected the colors of the lambs to be born – nevertheless, the mother herself no more creates the nature of her child than she creates herself.

Chapter 26, ¶ 5, line 3

Vocabulary – Write the vocabulary word on the first line (a help for spelling) followed by the definition.

1. Pomp

   _____ . _____

   _____

2. Forestall

   _____ . _____

   _____

3. Velleity

   _____ . _____

   _____

4. Enumerate

   _____ . _____

   _____

5. Vitiated

   _____ . _____

   _____

6. Progenitor

   _____ . _____

   _____

7. Extrinsic

   _____ . _____

   _____

8. Intrinsic

   _____ . _____

   _____

9. Variegated

   _____ . _____

   _____

Memorable Quote

The conclusion from all this is that God is never to be blamed for any defects that offend us, but should ever be praised for all the perfection we see in the natures He has made.

- Chapter 5 ¶ 2, page 250

Focus Passages

Book XIII, Chapter 1, (page 269) –

It is true that God did not endow man with the same nature that He gave to the angels – who could not possibly die even if they sinned – yet, had our first parents complied with the obligations of obedience, they, too, would have attained, without interruption of death, an immortality like that of the angels and an everlasting happiness.

Book XIII, Chapter 3, (page 271 – 272) –

Such was the greatness of the guilt that the punishment so impaired human nature that what was originally a penal condition for the first parents who sinned became a natural consequence in all of their descendants…

Hence, when the first couple were punished by the judgment of God, the whole human race, which was to become Adam's posterity through the first woman, was present in the first man. And what was born was not human nature as it was originally created but as it became after the first parents' sin and punishment – as far, at least as concerns the origin of sin and death…

what the first man became by perversion and penalty, this his descendants are by birth – natures subject to sin and death.

Book XIII, Chapter 4, (page 273) –

But now, by a greater and more wonderful grace of the Savior, the punishment of sin serves the purposes of sanctity. In the beginning, the first man was warned: 'If you sin, you shall die'; now, the martyr is admonished; 'Die that you may not sin.' The first man was told: 'If you transgress, you shall die the death'; now, the martyr is reminded: 'If you refuse death, you transgress the commandment.' What before was to be feared, if a man were to keep himself from sin, is now to be faced, if he is not to sin.

Book XIII, Chapter 17, (page 284) –

Since, then, these Platonists are so indulgent to their own suppositions, why do they refuse to believe that, by the will and power of God, even earthly bodies can be made immortal and that in these bodies, souls never separated by death nor ever burdened by their weight may live forever and in all felicity at least as well as their own gods can live in the bodies of fire and Jove, their king, in all the elements of matter. And if souls, in order to be blessed, must flee from every kind of body, then let their own gods flee from the starry spheres and let Jupiter escape from heaven and earth. Or, if that is beyond their powers, then let them be held to be unhappy.S

Our philosophers, however, do not want to face either of these alternatives: they do not dare to grant to their gods a separation from their bodies, for then it would seem that they were merely worshipping mortals; nor will they admit a privation of blessedness, for then they would have to acknowledge that their gods are miserable. To attain to blessedness, then, there is no need to be free of every kind of a body but only of those which are corruptible and irksome, burdensome and moribund, not such bodies as God, in His goodness, created for our first parents but only such were imposed as a punishment for sin.

Book XIII, Chapter 21, (page 288) –

No one should object to such reflections and others even more appropriate that might be made concerning the allegorical interpretation of the Garden of Eden, so long as we believe in the historical truth manifest in the faithful narrative of these events.

Chapter Summarization

Chapter One

_____

_____

_____

_____

Chapter Three

_____

_____

_____

_____

Chapter Four

_____

_____

_____

Chapter Seven

_____

_____

_____

_____

Chapter Summarization

Chapter Thirteen

_____

_____

_____

_____

Chapter Twenty-Four

_____

_____

_____

_____

Comprehension Questions

1. In chapter one Augustine discusses what he believes would have been the fate of Adam and Eve had they not sinned. What does he say would have happened to them?

2. Chapter three contains some of the most influential of Augustine's writing. Why does Augustine say that sin is transmitted to all humanity because of the sin of Adam?

3. In chapter four Augustine discusses the transformation of death. What is the difference of death for Adam and for the martyrs?

4. Augustine would certainly say that a person must be baptized in order to gain salvation. What does he have to say, though, about a martyr who has not been baptized?

5. In chapter thirteen Augustine gives an answer as to why there is such a battle between the soul and its desire to do good, and the body and its desire to do evil. How does Augustine explain the origin of this conflict?

6. In chapter twenty-four Augustine describes the difference between the body and the soul. One, he says, is better than the other. Describe his explanation.

7. In chapter twenty-four Augustine makes a distinction between the natural and the spiritual body. What is the difference, as stated by Augustine?

Vocabulary

However, in his person, human nature was so changed and vitiated that it suffers from the **recalcitrance** of a rebellious concupiscence and is bound by the law of death.

Chapter 3, ¶ 5, line 4

Thus, by the ineffable mercy of God, the penalty of sin is transformed into the **panoply** of virtue and the punishment of the sinner into the testing of a saint.

Chapter 4, ¶ 4, line 2

For, there is something harsh and unnatural in the violent **sundering** of what, in a living person, were so closely linked and interwoven; and the experience lasts until there is a complete loss of all feeling that depends on the union of soul and body.

Chapter 6, ¶ 1, line 3

Thus, in a word, while men are in the throes of death and death is bringing on disintegration, death is good for no one, but it may become **meritorious** if suffered to retain or to gain some good.

Chapter 8, ¶ 2, line 3

Thus, from a bad use of free choice, a sequence of misfortunes conducts the whole human race, excepting those redeemed by the grace of God, from the original **canker** in its root to the devastation of a second and endless death.

Chapter 14, ¶ 2, line 3

Since you have had a beginning, you cannot be immortal and indestructible; yet, by no means shall you ever suffer dissolution nor shall any decree of death destroy you, nor prevail over my determination which is a stronger pledge of your **perpetuity** than those bodies with which you were joined when you were brought into being.

Chapter 16, ¶ 4, line 12

This much, however, I think needed to be said in the face of those who are so proud of being, or of being called, Platonists that they are ashamed to be Christians, afraid that to share this name with ordinary people might taint the title of philosopher which they are so proud to share with a **coterie** so exclusive.

Chapter 16, ¶ 7, line 5

Since, then, these Platonists are so **indulgent** to their own **suppositions**, why do they refuse to believe that, by the will and power of God, even earthly bodies can be made immortal and that in these bodies, souls never separated by death nor ever burdened by their weight may live forever an in all felicity at least as well as their own gods can live in the bodies of fire and Jove, their king, in all the elements of matter.

Chapter 17, ¶ 7, lines 1 and 2

Vocabulary – Write the vocabulary word on the first line (a help for spelling) followed by the definition.

1. Recalcitrance

   _____. _____

   _____

2. Panoply

   _____. _____

   _____

3. Sundering

   _____. _____

   _____

4. Meritorious

   _____. _____

   _____

5. Canker

   _____. _____

   _____

6. Perpetuity

   _____. _____

   _____

7. Coterie

   _____. _____

   _____

8. Indulgent

   _____. _____

   _____

9. Suppositions

   _____. _____

   _____

Memorable Quote

Wickedness makes a bad use not only of evil, but of good. In the same way, holiness makes a good use not only of good, but also of evil.

- Chapter 5 ¶ 3, pages 274 – 275

Focus Passages

Book XIV, Chapter 3, (page 298) –

On the one hand, our corruptible body may be a burden on our soul; on the other hand, the cause of this encumbrance is not in the nature and substance of the body, and, therefore, aware as we are of its corruption, we do not desire to be divested of the body but rather to be clothed with its immortality. In immortal life we shall have a body, but it will no longer be a burden since it will no longer be corruptible. Now, however, 'the corruptible body is a load upon the soul, and the earthly habitation presseth down the mind that museth upon many things.' Yet, it is an error to suppose that all the evils of the soul proceed from the body.

Book XIV, Chapter 4, (pages 300 – 301) –

For, when we choose to sin, what we want is to get some good or get rid of something bad. The lie is in this, that what is done for our good ends in something bad, or what is done to make things better ends by making them worse. Why this paradox, except that the happiness of man can come not from himself but only from God, and that to live according to oneself is to sin, and to sin is to lose God? When, therefore, we said that two contrary and opposing cities arose because some men live according to the flesh and others live according to the spirit, we could equally well have said that they arose because some live according to man and others according to God.

Book XIV, Chapter 6, (page 304) –

It is clear, then, that the man who does not live according to man but according to God must be a lover of the good and, therefore, a hater of evil; since no man is wicked by nature but is wicked only by some defect, a man who lives according to God owes it to wicked men that his hatred be perfect, so that, neither hating the man because of his corruption nor loving the corruption because of the man, he should hate the sin but love the sinner. For, once the corruption has been cured, then all that is left should be loved and nothing remains to be hated.

Book XIV, Chapter 11, (page 305) –

Though we sometimes hear the expression, 'God changed His mind,' or even read in the figurative language of Scripture that 'God repented,' we interpret these sayings not in reference to the decisions determined on by Almighty God but in reference to the expectations of man or to the order of natural causes. So, we believe, as Scripture tells us, that God created man right and, therefore, endowed with a good will, for without a good will he would not have been 'right.'

Book XIV, Chapter Thirteen, (page 310) –

There is, then, a kind of lowliness which in some wonderful way causes the heart to be lifted up, and there is a kind of loftiness which makes the heart sink lower. This seems to be a sort of paradox, that loftiness should make something lower and lowliness lift something up. The reason for this is that holy lowliness makes us bow to what is above us and, since there is nothing above God, the kind of lowliness that makes us close to God exalts us.

Book XIV, Chapter Thirteen, (page 310) –

In fact, this is the main difference which distinguishes the two cities of which we are speaking. The humble City is the society of holy men and good angels; the proud city is the society of wicked men and evil angels. The one City began with the love of God; the other had its beginnings in the love of self.

Chapter Summarization

Chapter Two

_____

_____

_____

_____

Chapter Twelve

_____

_____

_____

_____

Chapter Thirteen

_____

_____

_____

_____

Chapter Fifteen

_____

_____

_____

_____

Chapter Summarization

Chapter Twenty-Six

_____

_____

_____

_____

Chapter Twenty-Eight

_____

_____

_____

_____

Comprehension Questions

1. In chapter two three Augustine writes that *it is an error to suppose that all the evils of the soul proceed from the body*. What does he mean by this statement?

2. Why, in chapter twelve, does Augustine say that the punishment for the sin of Adam was so great?

3. Why, in chapter thirteen, does Augustine say that Adam and Eve must have already fallen before they ate of the fruit that was forbidden to them?

4. In chapter thirteen Augustine describes the primary difference that distinguishes the City of God from the City of Men. What is this difference?

5. In chapter fifteen Augustine lists several reasons why the punishment for Adam's sin was just. What are his reasons?

6. Describe the perfect conditions in Eden that Augustine discusses in chapter twenty-six.

7. In chapter twenty-eight Augustine contrast the City of God and the City of Man. Summarize his comparisons.

Vocabulary

Finally, just as anyone who hears of sins or carnality (if I may use the word) immediately attributes them to the flesh, so no one doubts that sins of **animosity** belong to the mind.

Chapter 2, ¶ 2, line 37

On the one hand, our corruptible body may be a burden on our soul; on the other hand, the cause of this **encumbrance** is not in the nature and substance of the body, and, therefore, aware as we are of its corruption, we do not desire to be **divested** of the body but rather to be clothed with its immortality.

Chapter 3, ¶ 2, lines 2, 5 and 6

We ought not, therefore, to blame our sins and defects on the nature of the flesh, for this is to **disparage** the Creator.

Chapter 5, ¶ 2, line 2

So, subjecting it to his diabolical design by the powerful presence of his angelic nature and misusing it as his instrument, he, at first, **parleyed** cunningly with the woman as with the weaker part of that human society, hoping gradually to gain the whole.

Chapter 11, ¶ 9, line 9

There is a worse and more **execrable** kind of pride whereby one seeks the subterfuge of an excuse even when one's sin is manifest.

Chapter 14, ¶ 1, line 1

There were food and drink to keep away hunger and thirst and the tree of life to starve off death from **senescence**.

Chapter 26, ¶ 1, line 8

They could only be marked out by His grace; and how great that grace was they could see not only in their own deliverance but in the doom **meted** out to those who were not delivered from damnation.

Chapter 26, ¶ 4, line 13

It was because both in them and by means of them He could reveal how much was deserved by their guilt and condoned by His grace, and, also, because the harmony of the whole of reality which God has created and controls cannot be marred by the perverse **discordancy** of those who sin.

Chapter 26, ¶ 5, line 7

Vocabulary – Write the vocabulary word on the first line (a help for spelling) followed by the definition.

1. **Animosity**

   _____. _____

   _____

2. **Encumbrance**

   _____. _____

   _____

3. **Divested**

   _____. _____

   _____

4. **Disparage**

   _____. _____

   _____

5. **Parleyed**

   _____. _____

   _____

6. **Execrable**

   _____. _____

   _____

7. **Senescence**

   _____. _____

   _____

8. **Meted**

   _____. _____

   _____

9. **Discordancy**

   _____. _____

   _____

Memorable Quote

... he should hate the sin but love the sinner.

- Chapter 6 ¶ 3, page 304

Focus Passages

Book XV, Chapter 1, (page 323) –

In regard to mankind I have made a division. On the one side are those who live according to man; on the other, those who live according to God. And I have said that, in a deeper sense, we may speak of two cities or two human societies, the destiny of the one being an eternal kingdom under God while the doom of the other is eternal punishment along with the Devil.

Book XV, Chapter 5, (page 329) –

Unlike material possessions, goodness is not diminished when it is shared, either momentarily or permanently, with others, but expands and, in fact, the more heartily each of the lovers of goodness enjoys the possession the more does goodness grow. What is more, goodness is not merely a possession that no one can maintain who is unwilling to share it, but it is one that increases the more its possessor loves to share it.

Book XV, Chapter 7, (page 333) –

Here we have the very heart of the earthly city. Its God (or gods) is he or they who will help the city to victory after victory and to a reign of earthly peace; and this city worships, not because it has any love for service, but because its passion is for domination. This, in fact, is the difference between good men and bad men, that the former make use of the world in order to enjoy God, whereas the latter would like to make use of God in order to enjoy the world – if, or course, they believe in God and His providence over man, and are not so bad as those who deny even this.

Book XV, Chapter 14, (page 349) –

But for the moment I must draw my present argument to its conclusion. It is this: There is no reason to doubt that, in an age when the life-span was so long, a great city could have been built by the first-born son of the first man, Adam. It was, indeed, merely an earthly city; it was not that city called the City of God which it is my main purpose to describe and which moved me to undertake the toilsome task of writing this very big Book.

Book XV, Chapter 21 (pages 361 – 362) –

The chronology of the two cities is begun only when both cities have been presented to the reader as issuing from that single gate of our mortality which Adam opened. One is the city of 'belongings' here in this world; the other is the city of 'longings' for God. Once started on their way, they take different roads, each to the proper doom or destiny it deserves. One undated sequence of generations is given, but all generations are traced back to Adam, out of whom, as out of a single mass of damaged clay thrown on a waste-heap, God fashions two kinds of pottery: the vessels fashioned by His wrath and fit only for contempt and the vessels made by His mercy and meant to be honored. To the former He pays in punishment the doom they earn; to the latter He bestows, as a gift of grace, a destiny they never could have deserved. God's purpose in this is that the heavenly City, during its exile on earth, by contrasting itself with the vessels of wrath, should learn not to expect too much from the freedom of the power of choice, but should trust in the 'hope to call upon the name of the Lord God.' It is true, indeed, that the human will resides in a nature that was created good because its Creator is good, but that nature is mutable even though its Maker is immutable, for the simple reason that it was made out of nothing. Therefore, when the will turns from the good and does evil, it does so by the freedom of its own choice, but when it turns from evil and does good, it does so only with the help of God.

Chapter Summarization

Chapter One

_____

_____

_____

_____

Chapter Two

_____

_____

_____

Chapter Four

_____

_____

_____

Chapter Seven

_____

_____

_____

Chapter Summarization

Chapter Seventeen

_____

_____

_____

_____

Chapter Twenty-One

_____

_____

_____

_____

Chapter Twenty-Six

_____

_____

_____

_____

Comprehension Questions

1. In chapter one Augustine draws a parallel between Cain and Abel and the City of God. What is the parallel?

2. In chapter two Augustine says there are two forms – one is a visible appearance of the earthly city and the other is a shadow of the heavenly City. Who are these two who represent the two cities?

3. Augustine, in chapter four, recognizes some good in the City of Man. What does he say is good in this city?

4. In chapter seven Augustine discusses the sin of Cain. Although the book of Genesis does not give any specifics as to why God was not pleased with the sacrifice of Cain, Augustine shares what he believes to be the answer. What is Augustine's theory on this matter and where does he find his clue?

5. After several chapters of discussing whether the early Biblical years were the same length as present, Augustine presents his final conclusion to this question in chapter fourteen. What is Augustine's answer regarding the length of the Biblical year?

6. In chapter seventeen Augustine discusses the meaning of the names of Cain, Henoch, Seth, and Enos. What does each name mean and what interpretation does Augustine give to their names?

7. Augustine notes in chapter twenty-one that in Genesis 5 the writer begins the genealogy of Noah back at Adam. What is the significance of this for Augustine?

Vocabulary

The discussion could be pursued in greater detail, but it would raise so many and such varied problems that I would need for their solution more books than our present purpose calls for; nor is there so much time at my disposal that I feel obliged to waste it in satisfying the curiosity of those persons with nothing to do who are more **captious** in putting their questions than capable of grasping the answers.
Chapter 1, ¶ 1, line 12

It need not surprise us, then, that long afterwards, in the founding of that city which was to dominate so many peoples and become the capital of that earthly city with which I am dealing, the copy, so to speak, corresponded to the original – to what the Greeks call the **archetype**.
Chapter 5, ¶ 1, line 8

The **dispensation** by which He knows the one from the other is profoundly deep, yet no less just.
Chapter 6, ¶ 4, line 2

The other days added were said by the Romans to be **intercalated** to fill out the full solar year.
Chapter 12, ¶ 1, line 21

To clinch their argument, those who hold that the Biblical year was reckoned differently from ours **adduce** the testimony of many historians to the effect, for example, that the Egyptians had a year of four months, the Acarnanians one of six, the Lavinians a year of thirteen months.
Chapter 12, ¶ 2, line 2

Where mere numbers do not focus attention on something which in itself is easy to understand or useful to know, they are merely transcribed with accuracy, and mistakes once made are still more rarely **emended**.
Chapter 13, ¶ 3, line 13

In fact, I have noticed how rarely custom allows even in our days what is permissible in law, namely, marriages between first cousins, who are the nearest in **consanguinity** after brothers and sisters.
Chapter 16, ¶ 4, line 18

On this matter of sacrifices, I have pointed out in some of the previous Books that the reason why the demons, who **arrogate** to themselves divinity and seek to be recognized as gods, demand sacrifices and delight in such worship is that they know that true sacrifice is due to the true God.
Chapter 16, ¶ 6, line 15

But, whatever may have been the arrangement in regard to the line of succession from Cain, whether it went by **primogeniture** or by chosen kings, there is one circumstance which seem to me so important that it must be mentioned, namely, that, besides Lamech, whose name is listed seventh after Adam, there were enough names mentioned, including the three sons and one daughter, to bring the total up to eleven, the number which is a symbol of sin.
Chapter 20, ¶ 8, lines 2 – 3

Vocabulary – Write the vocabulary word on the first line (a help for spelling) followed by the definition.

1. Captious

   _____ · _____

   _____

2. Archetype

   _____ · _____

   _____

3. Dispensation

   _____ · _____

   _____

4. Intercalated

   _____ · _____

   _____

5. Adduce

   _____ · _____

   _____

6. Emended

   _____ · _____

   _____

7. Consanguinity

   _____ · _____

   _____

8. Arrogate

   _____ · _____

   _____

9. Primogeniture

   _____ · _____

   _____

Memorable Quote

The fact is that the power to reach domination by war is not the same as the power to remain in perpetual control.

- Chapter 4 ¶ 1, page 327

Focus Passages

Book XVI, Chapter 7, (page 364) –

In this case, if the earth produced the many animals in islands which could not be reached, it becomes clearer than ever that the purpose of all the animals in the ark was less for the sake of replenishing the stock of animals than for the sake of prefiguring the mystery of the Church which was to be composed of so many people.

Book XVI, Chapter 9, (page 367) –

As to the nonsense about there being *antipodae*, that is to say, men living on the far side of the earth, where the sun rises when it sets for us, men who have their feet facing ours when they walk – that is utterly incredible. No one pretends to have any factual information, but a hypothesis is reached by the argument that, since the earth is suspended between the celestial hemispheres and since the universe must have a similar lowest and central point, therefore the other portion of the earth which is below us cannot be without human inhabitants.

One flaw in the argument is that, even if the universe could be proved by reasoning to be shaped like a round globe – or at least believed to be so – it does not follow that the other hemisphere of the earth must appear above the surface of the ocean; or if it does, there is no immediate necessity why it should be inhabited by men.

Book XVI, Chapter 17, (pages 371- 372) –

It was in Assyria, then, that the domination of the godless city was at its height. The capital was Babylon – the best of all names for the city of the earth-born, since Babylon means 'confusion' . . . This was about 1,200 years before the founding of Rome – which, if I may say so, was to be a second Babylon in the West.

Book XVI, Chapter 42, (page 374) –

What Jacob is here doing is to point to the two famous promises. For, one of the sons is to be the father of a 'people' and the other of a 'multitude of nations,' and nothing could be clearer than that these two promises refer to the people of Israel and the whole world filled with the sons of Abraham, the 'people' being sons according to the flesh and 'the multitude of nations' being sons according to the faith.

Book XVI, Chapter 43, (pages 375 – 376) –

This occurred soon after the departure from Egypt, when the people were beginning their wanderings in the desert, on the fiftieth day after the Pasch was celebrated by the sacrifice of a lamb. Not only is this lamb a perfect symbolic prophecy of Christ passing, through the sacrifice of His passion, from this world to the Father – I need hardly recall that *pascha* is the Hebrew for 'passing,' – but in the period of revelation of the New Covenant, it was on the fiftieth day after Christ our Pasch was offered up in the sacrifice that the Holy Spirit came down from heaven.

Book XVI, Chapter 43, (page 377) –

Thus we may say that before Abraham the people of God were in their childhood from Noe to Abraham, the period in which they were identified by their speaking the Hebrew language. For, a human being begins to speak in childhood, the age following infancy – which is derived from the Latin, *infans*, meaning unable to speak. Infancy is a period the memory of which is lost, much as all memory of the infancy of the human race was lost in the flood.

Chapter Summarization

Chapter Seven

_____

_____

_____

_____

Chapter Ten

_____

_____

_____

Chapter Seventeen

_____

_____

_____

Chapter Forty-Two

_____

_____

_____

_____

Chapter Summarization

Chapter Forty-Three

Comprehension Questions

1. In chapter seven Augustine discusses how it might have been possible for wild animals to reach distant islands after the flood. What possible solutions to this question does he raise?

2. In chapter ten Augustine mentions two proofs of human pride, which forms the basis of the City of Man. What are these two proofs?

3. In chapter ten Augustine mentions the Septuagint. What is this book?

4. In chapter seventeen Augustine names three famous pagan empires. What are they? Which was the most powerful and what was its capital?

5. In chapter forty-two Augustine sees Esau and Jacob and the two sons of Joseph as symbolizing two different peoples. In Augustine's opinion, who do they symbolize?

6. In chapter forty-three Augustine refers to the Pasch. What is the Pasch?

7. In chapter forty-three Augustine compares the time period of Noah to Abraham to what stage of a person's life?

Vocabulary

In this case, if the earth produced the many animals in islands which could not be reached, it becomes clearer than ever that the purpose of all the animals in the ark was less for the sake of replenishing the stock of animals than for the sake of **prefiguring** the mystery of the Church which was to be composed of so many people
Chapter 7, ¶ 1, line 22

For, if we did not know that apes, monkeys and baboons are not humans, but animals, historians, eager to show off the curiosity of their knowledge, might falsely and with **impunity** describe them as human.
Chapter 8, ¶ 7, line 14

As to the nonsense about there being ***antipodae***, that is to say, men living on the far side of the earth, where the sun rises when it sets for us, men who have their feet facing ours when they walk – that is utterly incredible.
Chapter 9, ¶ 1, line 1

Other matters we may touch on briefly and in passing if some special **pertinence** requires it.
Chapter 10, ¶ 3, line 6

Note the preceding words: 'God looked down from heaven on the children of men, to see if there were any that did not understand, or did seek God,' and then the words that follow prove that all the sons of man, that is, all who belong to the city that lives according to men and not according to God are **reprobate**.
Chapter 10, ¶ 6, line 34

And 'his eyes are red from wine' means that these eyes full of His spirit have been **inebriated** by His chalice, of which the Psalmist sings: 'And thy chalice that inebriates, how excellent it is.'

It was then that Moses was snatched by **stealth** from the hands of the executioners and found a home in the royal palace, for God's providence had great things for him to do.
Chapter 43, ¶ 1, line 7

At last, the spirit of the Egyptians was broken by so many **grievous** afflictions and the Israelites were freed.
Chapter 43, ¶ 1, line 25

He was **deposed** and defeated in battle, and his heirs were rejected as candidates for the crown.
Chapter 43, ¶ 6, line 2

Vocabulary – Write the vocabulary word on the first line (a help for spelling) followed by the definition.

1. Prefiguring

   _____ . _____

   _____

2. Impunity

   _____ . _____

   _____

3. Antipodae

   _____ . _____

   _____

4. Pertinence

   _____ . _____

   _____

5. Reprobate

   _____ . _____

   _____

6. Inebriated

   _____ . _____

   _____

7. Stealth

   _____ . _____

   _____

8. Grievous

   _____ . _____

   _____

9. Deposed

   _____ . _____

   _____

Memorable Quote

This was about 1,200 years before the founding of Rome – which, if I may say so, was to be a second Babylon in the West.

- Chapter 17 ¶ 4, page 372

Focus Passages

Book XVII, Chapter 1, (page 378) –
There is a period which begins with the prophecies of Samuel and continues through the seventy years of the Babylonian captivity (which Jeremias had foretold) and ends with the rebuilding of the Temple, after the Israelites came home. This period is known as the 'Age of the Prophets," although, of course, the Patriarch Noe, in whose lifetime the whole earth was destroyed by the flood, and others before and after him up to the time of the kings, were Prophets also. At least, they prefigured, in some fashion, many things touching the City of God and the kingdom of heaven, and sometimes actually prophesied. Consequently, it is not too much to speak of these men as Prophets; some of them are explicitly so called in Holy Writ, for example, Abraham and Moses.

Book XVII, Chapter 2, (page 379) –
I have already related how, out of all the promises God made from the beginning, two were made to Abraham. One was that his seed should own the land of Chanaan, for such is the sense of the words: 'Come into the land which I shall show thee, and I will make of thee a great nation.' The other, which is vastly more important than the first, was that, whereas in his fleshly seed he was to be the father of every people that would follow in the footsteps of his faith. This promise opens with the words: 'In you shall the nations of the earth be blessed.'

Book XVII, Chapter 3, (page 381) –
Thus, the Prophets' sayings are of three classes: one class refers to the earthly, a second to the heavenly Jerusalem, and a third to both simultaneously. It will be best to support this assertion with illustrations. The Prophet Nathan was sent to accuse King David of a grave sin and to foretell what evils were to befall him on this account. Now no one can fail to see that this prophecy refers to the earthly city. There are others like it, sometimes addressed to the people at large for their profit and well-being, and sometimes to an individual who merited a word from God to foreknow some event for the guidance of his temporal life.

Book XVII, Chapter 16, (page 386) –
In this passage the reader hears one spoken of as God whose throne is for ever and ever, one anointed by God – as God anoints, of course, with a spiritual chrism visible only to the eyes of faith. Now, is there any reader – however dull-witted – who does not recognize in this person the Christ whom we preach, in whom we believe? Is there any insider so ill-informed in his faith, any outsider so deaf to its universally known character, as not to be aware that Christ's very name is derived from 'chrism,' that is, from His anointing?

Book XVII, Chapter 16, (page 388) –
Accordingly, we must say that Christ as God founded this City in the Patriarchs and Prophets, even before, as a man, He became, through Mary, a citizen.

Book XVII, Chapter 16, (page 388) –
These truths are perfectly clear and, therefore, any interpretations of other parts of the psalm, which are somewhat obscure by reason of metaphorical language, must be consistent with what we know to be true.

Chapter Summarization

Chapter One

_____

_____

_____

Chapter Two

_____

_____

_____

Chapter Three

_____

_____

_____

Chapter Fourteen

_____

_____

_____

_____

Chapter Summarization

Chapter Fifteen

_____

_____

_____

_____

Chapter Sixteen

_____

_____

_____

_____

Comprehension Questions

1. When was the 'Age of the Prophets' as described by Augustine in chapter one?

2. In chapter two Augustine discusses two promises to Abraham. What are the two promises and what does the second promise represent?

3. What are the three classes of prophecy as described by Augustine in chapter three?

4. How does the music of David represent the City of God, as Augustine explains in chapter fourteen?

5. In chapter fifteen Augustine explains how the psalms prophesy about Jesus and the Church, but he only uses one psalm as an example. Why doesn't he use more examples from the book of Psalms?

6. In chapter sixteen Augustine names the founder of the City of God. Who is the founder?

7. In chapter twenty-four Augustine mentions that after Malachias, Aggeus, Zacharias, and Esdras there were no more prophets until the time of the coming of Jesus. Who were the prophets at the time of Jesus?

Vocabulary

And so as far as I am able, I shall so govern my pen that, God willing, I may get through this Book, neither leaving out what should be said nor lingering on what is **superfluous**.
Chapter 1, ¶ 4, line 19

However, I do not **censure** those who may have been able to carve out some spiritual interpretation from every historical fact recounted, so long as they take good care first and foremost to adhere to the historical fact.
Chapter 3, ¶ 8, line 1

This opinion, however, is rendered **untenable** by our Saviour Himself, who says in the Gospel that David in the Spirit calls Christ his Lord.
Chapter 14, ¶ 2, line 7

No **insuperable** difficulty for this position is raised by the fact that some psalms bear the names of Prophets who lived long after David's day and even seem to present them as speakers.
Chapter 14, ¶ 4, line 1

Besides, since the sense of any one verse should be supported by the pattern of the whole psalm or, at least, should not be contradicted by the context, I may appear to be **arbitrarily** plucking texts out of their context to bolster my own views, like a man who makes a patchwork of verses on a theme quite unlike that of the longer poem from which the verses have been **culled**.
Chapter 15, ¶ 1, lines 15 and 18

To show the valid use of any excerpt, the entire psalm must be **expounded**.
Chapter 15, ¶ 1, line 19

'My heart hath uttered a good word; I speak my words to the king; my tongue is the pen of a **scrivener** that writeth swiftly.
Chapter 16, ¶ 2, line 2

In this passage the reader hears one spoken of as God whose throne is for ever and ever, one anointed by God – as God anoints, of course, with a spiritual **chrism** visible only to the eyes of faith.
Chapter 16, ¶ 3, line 3

Vocabulary – Write the vocabulary word on the first line (a help for spelling) followed by the definition.

1. Superfluous

   _____ . _____

2. Censure

   _____

   _____ . _____ _____

   _____ . _____ _____

3. Untenable

   _____ . _____

   _____

4. Insuperable

   _____ . _____

   _____

5. Arbitrarily

   _____ . _____

   _____

6. Culled

   _____ . _____

   _____

7. Expounded

   _____ . _____

   _____

8. Scrivener

   _____ . _____

   _____

9. Chrism

   _____ . _____

   _____

Memorable Quote

Accordingly, we must say that Christ as God founded this City in the Patriarchs and Prophets, even before, as a man, He became, through Mary, a citizen.

- Chapter 16 ¶ 8, page 388

Focus Passages
Book XVIII, Chapter 41, (page 411 – 412)

How differently has that other race, that other commonwealth of men, that other City, the people of Israel, to whom was entrusted the word of God, managed matters! No broadminded, muddle-headed mixing of true prophets with false prophets there! They have recognized and held as the true-speaking authors of Holy Writ only those who are in perfect harmony with one another. These writers are for them their philosophers, that is, their lovers of wisdom, their sages, their theologians, their prophets, their teachers of good living and right believing – all in one. They know that if they think and live according to what these men taught, they are thinking and living according to God – who spoke through the inspired writers – and not according to man.

Book XVIII, Chapter 51, (page 418 – 419) –

Actually, all foes of the Church, whether blinded by error or moved by malice, subserve her in some fashion. If they have power to do her physical harm, they develop her power to suffer; if they oppose her intellectually, they bring out her wisdom; since she must love even her enemies, her loving kindness is made manifest; and whether she has to deal with them in the persuasiveness of argument or the chastisement of law, they bring into play her power to do good.

So it is that the diabolical prince of the ungodly city is not allowed to harm the pilgrim City of God, even when he stirs up his tools and dupes against her. Beyond all doubt, Divine Providence sees to it that she has both some solace of prosperity that she may not be broken by adversity and some testing of adversity that she may not be weakened by prosperity. Thus, the one balances the other, as one can see from the words of the psalm, 'According to the multitude of sorrows in my heart, so thy consolations have gladdened my soul,' and those of St. Paul: 'Rejoicing in hope, being patient in tribulation.'

Book XVIII, Chapter 53, (pages 420 - 421) –

At this point people usually inquire: When will all this happen? A most unreasonable question, for, if it were good for us to know the answer, the Master, God Himself, would have told His disciples when they asked Him. When they had Him face to face, they did not receive such news in silence, either, but plainly asked Him: 'Lord wilt thou at this time restore the kingdom to Israel?' And He replied: 'It is not for you to know the times or dates which the Father has fixed by his own authority' – an answer, it should be noted, given to men who had not sought to know the exact hour, or day, or year, but only the general time of this fulfillment. Obviously, then, it is a waste of effort for us to attempt counting the precise number of years which this world has yet to go, since we know from the mouth of Truth that it is none of our business…

Suffice it to say that the fingers of all such calculators were slackened by Him who imposed silence with the words: 'It is not for you to know the times or dates which the Father has fixed by his own authority.'

Book XVIII, Chapter 54, (page 425) –

Let me, at long last, end this Book. I have described in such detail as I judged adequate the historical course of the two cities, the heavenly and the earthly, intermingled as they have been from the beginning and are to be until the end of time. The earthly one has made for herself, according to her heart's desire, false gods out of any sources at all, even out of human beings, that she might adore them with sacrifices. The heavenly one, on the other hand, living like a wayfarer in this world, makes no false gods for herself. On the contrary, she herself is made by the true God that she may be herself a true sacrifice to Him

Both of these cities alike make use of temporal goods and both are equally afflicted by temporal ills – but how different they are in faith, how dissimilar in hope, how unlike in love! This will go on until they are to be separated in the Last Judgment, when each shall achieve its appointed end – an end which will have no end.

Chapter Summarization

Chapter Two

_____

_____

_____

_____

Chapter Nine

_____

_____

_____

_____

Chapter Twenty-Three

_____

_____

_____

_____

Chapter Forty

_____

_____

_____

_____

Chapter Summarization

Chapter Forty-One

_____

_____

_____

_____

_____

Chapter Forty-Two

_____

_____

_____

_____

Chapter Fifty-One

_____

_____

_____

_____

Chapter Fifty-Four

_____

_____

_____

_____

Comprehension Questions

1. In chapter two Augustine says only one thing can satisfy human nature. What is that one thing?

2. Augustine writes in chapter nine about the punishments given to the women of Athens by Neptune for choosing Minerva. What were those punishments?

3. In chapter twenty-three Augustine writes of the acrostic Ichthus, which is the Greek word for fish. What does the acrostic Ichthus mean?

4. Augustine writes strongly against the philosophers of the earthly city in chapters forty and forty-one. He writes of why he believes the philosophers can never provide real truth to humanity. What is Augustine's basis for this claim and what is his proof for why the Church does have the truth?

5. In chapter forty-two Augustine discusses the translation of the Septuagint. Who authorized the translation of the Septuagint?

6. In chapter fifty-one Augustine writes that suffering and persecution has a positive effect upon the Church. According to Augustine, how does suffering and persecution benefit the church?

7. In chapter fifty-four Augustine is reacting to followers of pagan religions who supposedly had a text that prophesied that Christianity would last only 365 years. In his refutation, Augustine points to several events that could be used as the starting point of Christianity. What are these starting points, and which one does he choose as the most accurate starting point? Why is this important to Augustine?

Vocabulary

The vanquished succumb to the victorious, preferring sheer survival and any kind of peaceful settlement to their own continued **hegemony** – even to liberty itself.
Chapter 2, ¶ 1, line 15

Varro goes on to say that the men of Athens, to **placate** him, decreed a three-fold punishment for their womenfolk; they were to lose the right of **suffrage**; they were not to give their own names to their children; they were never to be known as Athenians.
Chapter 9, ¶ 1, lines 20 and 22

But these could not have been wars **fraught** with such harrowing difficulties, because the nations at that time were still unschooled in self-defense; neither were they as populous and powerful as they later became.
Chapter 22, ¶ 1, line 12

Quite to the contrary, it speaks out so openly against them and their **votaries** that the prophetess herself, it seems, must be counted among those who belonged to the City of God.
Chapter 23, ¶ 4, line 5

So far as writings are concerned, however, they **bequeathed** nothing to posterity, save Solon, who is reputed to have given the Athenians some laws, and Thales, who left books on the principles of natural philosophy.
Chapter 25, ¶ 2, line 10

In a word, it is because they might be **spurious** that they are not to be trusted; and this is pre-eminently the case with works that contain declarations that run counter to the faith as contained in canonical writings, for then we can be absolutely sure that the attribution is spurious.
Chapter 38, ¶ 5, line 6

Granted that there is a more **copious** literary legacy in philosophy, a man still would be hard put to find, in all this abundance, any philosophers in agreement on everything they have taught – a proposition, however, which I cannot take time to prove in this work.
Chapter 41, ¶ 2, line 15

Beyond all doubt, Divine Providence sees to it that she has both some **solace** of prosperity that she may not be broken by adversity and some testing of adversity that she may not be weakened by prosperity.
Chapter 51, ¶ 3, line 4

Vocabulary – Write the vocabulary word on the first line (a help for spelling) followed by the definition.

1. **Hegemony**

   _____. _____

   _____

2. **Placate**

   _____. _____

   _____. _____

3. **Suffrage**

   _____. _____

   _____

4. **Fraught**

   _____. _____

   _____

5. **Votaries**

   _____. _____

   _____

6. **Bequeathed**

   _____. _____

   _____

7. **Spurious**

   _____. _____

   _____

8. **Copious**

   _____. _____

   _____

9. **Solace**

   _____. _____

   _____

Memorable Quote

Beyond all doubt, Divine Providence sees to it that she has both some solace of prosperity that she may not be broken by adversity and some testing of adversity that she may not be weakened by prosperity.

- Chapter 51 ¶ 3, page 419

Focus Passages

Book XIX Chapter 4, (page 437) –

Those who think that the supreme good and evil are to found in this life are mistaken. It makes no difference whether it is in the body or in the soul or in both – or, specifically, in pleasure or virtue or in both – that they seek the supreme good. They seek in vain whether they look to serenity, to virtue, or to both; whether to pleasure plus serenity, or to virtue, or to all three; or to the satisfaction of our innate exigencies, or to virtue, o to both. It is in vain that men look for beatitude on earth or in human nature.

Book XIX, Chapter 7, (page 447) –

I know the objection that a good ruler will wage wars only if they are just. But, surely, if he will only remember that he is a man, he will begin by bewailing the necessity he is under of waging even just wars. A good man would be under compulsion to wage no wars at all, if there were not such things as just wars. A just war, moreover, is justified only by the injustice of an aggressor; and that injustice ought to be a source of grief to any good man, because it is human injustice. It would be deplorable in itself, apart from being a source of conflict.

Book XIX, Chapter 14, (page 460) –

Meanwhile, God teaches him two chief commandments, the love of God and the love of neighbor. In these precepts man finds three beings to love, namely, God, himself, and his fellow man, and knows that he is not wrong in loving himself so long as he loves God. As a result, he must help his neighbor (whom he is obliged to love as himself) to love God. Thus, he must help his wife, children, servants, and all others whom he can influence. He must wish, moreover, to be similarly helped by his fellow man, in case he himself needs such assistance. Out of all this love he will arrive at peace, as much as in him lies, with every man – at that human peace which is regulated fellowship. Right order here means, first, that he harm no one, and, second, that he help whomever he can. His fundamental duty is to look out for his own home, for both by natural and human law he has easier and readier access to their requirements.

Book XIX, Chapter 17, (page 465) –

So long, then as the heavenly City is wayfaring on earth, she invites citizens from all nations and all tongues, and unites them into a single pilgrim band. She takes no issue with that diversity of customs, laws, and traditions whereby human peace is sought and maintained. Instead of nullifying or tearing down, she preserves and appropriates whatever in the diversities of divers races is aimed at one and the same objective of human peace, provided only that they do not stand in the way of the faith and worship of the one supreme and true God.

Book XIX, Chapter 23, (pages 477 – 478) –

To sum up. Where justice is wanting, in the sense that the civil community does not take its orders from the one supreme God, and follow them out with the help of His grace; where sacrifice is offered to any save Him alone; where, consequently, the civil community is not such that everyone obeys God in this respect; where the soul does not control the body, and reason our evil urges, as proper order and faith require; where neither the individuals nor the whole community, 'the people,' live by that faith of the just which works through that charity which loves God as He should be loved and one's neighbor as oneself – where this kind of justice is lacking, I maintain, there does not exist 'a multitude bound together by a mutual recognition of rights and a mutual co-operation for the common good.' This being so, there is no proper 'people' – if Scipio's definition is correct – nor a commonwealth. For, where there is no 'people,' there is no 'people's' weal.

Chapter Summarization

Chapter One

_____

_____

_____

Chapter Six

_____

_____

_____

Chapter Seven

_____

_____

_____

Chapter Thirteen

_____

_____

_____

Chapter Summarization

Chapter Fifteen

_____

_____

_____

_____

Chapter Twenty-One

_____

_____

_____

_____

Chapter Twenty-Seven

_____

_____

_____

_____

Comprehension Questions

1. In chapter one Augustine discusses the four ends which men naturally pursue. What are these four ends?

2. What is the problem with justice as discussed by Augustine in chapter six?

3. What are the three stages in human hierarchy that Augustine discusses in chapter seven?

4. What are the different kinds of peace as related by Augustine in chapter thirteen?

5. In chapter fifteen Augustine describes why he believes some people live in slavery and under the dominion of others. What is his reason for believing this?

6. In chapter twenty-one Augustine says that *there never existed any such thing as a Roman Republic* (page 468). Why does he make this statement?

7. In chapter twenty-seven Augustine contrasts the life of virtue in this world with the final peace that will be present in eternity. Describe how he contrasts the two.

Vocabulary

Finally, there have been philosophers who pursued quite different ends as being ultimates – some, virtue; others, pleasure – yet observed the **idiosyncrasies** of life that gave the Cynics their name.
Chapter 1, ¶ 13, line 3

And when we seek final rest in the supreme good, what do we seek save an end to this conflict between flesh and spirit, freedom from this **propensity** to evil against which the spirit is at war?
Chapter 4, ¶ 6, line 11

Varro also makes the **egregious** mistake of maintaining that this life is still the happy life in spite of evils so grievous that, for one who suffers them, suicide becomes imperative.
Chapter 4, ¶ 11, line 4

Even when the **frays** are over, there is never any freedom from fear.
Chapter 5, ¶ 3, line 5

In the midst of their agonies the evil and the godless weep for the loss of their nature's goods, knowing, meanwhile, that God whose great generosity they **contemned** was perfectly just when he took these goods away.
Chapter 13, ¶ 5, line 18

If no crime had ever been **perpetrated** against this law, there would be no crime to repress with the penalty of enslavement.
Chapter 15, ¶ 3, line 15

Those who are true fathers are as **solicitous** for everyone in their households as for their own children to worship and to be worthy of God.
Chapter 16, ¶ 2, line 1

Instead of **nullifying** or tearing down, she preserves and appropriates whatever in the diversities of divers races is aimed at one and the same objective of human peace, provided only that they do not stand in the way of the faith and worship of the one supreme and true God.
Chapter 17, ¶ 5, line 5

But let us come now to his more candid **avowals**, and hear how great he makes the God of the Jews out to be.
Chapter 23, ¶ 3, line 1

Vocabulary – Write the vocabulary word on the first line (a help for spelling) followed by the definition.

1. **Idiosyncrasies**

_____ . _____

_____

2. **Propensity**

_____ . _____

_____

3. **Egregious**

_____ . _____

_____

4. **Frays**

_____ . _____

_____

5. **Contemned**

_____ . _____

_____

6. **Perpetrated**

_____ . _____

_____

7. **Solicitous**

_____ . _____

_____

8. **Nullifying**

_____ . _____

_____

9. **Avowals**

_____ . _____

_____

Memorable Quote

Even so, however, no one should give up entirely his delight in learning...

- Chapter 19 ¶ 4, page 468

Focus Passages

Book XX, Chapter 1, (page 484) –

So, too, human beings – whether manifestly or hiddenly, whether in this life or later – pay a divinely assessed penalty, each for his or her own personal wrongdoing. And it is right to speak of penalty and reward even though no positively good action can be done without divine help, and although there can be no sin of man or angel without a divine permission which is at the same time a perfectly just judgment.

Book XX, Chapter 2, (page 484 – 485) –

While time lasts, however, we are schooled to bear misfortune calmly, for good and bad men without distinction have to bear it; and we set no great store by prosperity, since bad and good men alike may come to enjoy it. So it is that, even in these temporal vicissitudes where God's justice is not apparent, divine Revelation must save us from confusion.

We cannot know, for example, what secret decree of God's justice makes this good man poor and that bad man rich; why this man, whose immoral life should cause him, in our estimation, to be torn with grief, is, in point of fact, quite happy; why that man, whose praiseworthy life should bring him joy, is, in fact, sad of soul; why this innocent party leaves the courtroom not just avenged but actually condemned, unfairly treated by a corrupt judge or overwhelmed by lying testimony, while his guilty opponent not merely gets off unpunished but goes gloating over his vindication. Here we have an irreligious man in excellent health, there a holy man wasting away to a shadow with disease. Here are some young men, robbers by profession, in superb physical fettle; there, some mere babies, unable to harm anyone even in speech, afflicted with various kinds of implacable disease. A very much needed man is swept off by untimely death; a man who, we think, should not even have been born survives him and lives a long life. One man loaded with crimes is lifted to honors, while another whose life is beyond reproach lives under a cloud of suspicion. And so of innumerable other examples.

Book XX, Chapter 30, (page 490) –

The conclusion, then, is that, when we read in the prophetical books that 'God' is to come to pronounce the last judgment, we do not need any indication more specific than the mention of the judgment to realize that it is Christ who is meant.

Book XX, Chapter 30, (page 492) –

In connection with the last judgment, therefore, we who believe can be sure of the following truths: Elias the Thesbite will return; the Jews will believe; Antichrist will persecute the Church; Christ will be the judge; the dead will rise; the good will be separated from the wicked; the world will suffer from fire, but will be renewed. Of course, what we believe is the simple fact that all these things are to be; but how and in what sequence the events are to occur we must leave to future experience, which alone can teach these truths so much better than human intelligence can at present understand. My own view is that they will occur in the order I have just written.

Book XX, Chapter 30, (page 492 – 493) –

Men, however, who are wise with the wisdom of God hold that the irrefutable omnipotence of God is an unanswerable argument in favor of all of these predictions which seem too incredible to human intelligence but which are contained in holy writings whose veracity has now been established in countless ways. Men whose wisdom is according to God hold for certain, first, that God in the Scriptures could not possibly lie, and, second, that He has the power to do things that seem impossible to the unbeliever.

Chapter Summarization

Chapter One

_____

_____

_____

_____

Chapter Two

_____

_____

_____

Chapter Thirty

_____

_____

_____

Comprehension Questions

1. In chapter one Augustine talks about the good and righteous judgment of God. What does this kind of judgment entail?

2. In chapter one Augustine says that God judges men and angels in two ways. What are the two ways in which God judges?

3. In chapter two Augustine reaches a conclusion about the question of why good or ill fortune is visited without distinction upon good and bad men. What is his conclusion?

4. In chapter thirty, as Augustine discusses the prophesies of the final judgment of Christ, what phrase does he say makes it *obvious that Christ is meant*?

5. In chapter thirty Augustine compares a verse in both the Vulgate and Septuagint translations. Though the Septuagint is his preferred translation, why does he combine the two translations when referring to this particular verse?

6. Augustine says in chapter thirty that *peoples everywhere on the earth* have faith in Christ, but at one time it was hardly anyone but one person who demonstrated this faith. Who was this one person?

7. In chapter thirty Augustine gives his reason for why some people doubt the truth of the coming of Christ and His judgment, as foretold in Scripture. What is the reason Augustine gives for their doubt?

Vocabulary

In both cases, the reasonings are human, **specious** and false
Chapter 1, ¶ 1, line 8

For there is no human being, I think, who will withhold **assent**, if only he will take these texts at their face value and realize that the holy men who wrote them were inspired by the true and supreme God.
Chapter 1, ¶ 1, line 9

Here are some young men, robbers by profession, in superb physical **fettle**; there, some mere babies, unable to harm anyone even in speech, afflicted with various kinds of **implacable** disease.
Chapter 2, ¶ 2, lines 13 and 15

The whole arrangement makes God's judgments all the more **inscrutable** and His ways unsearchable.
Chapter 2, ¶ 3, line 19

Suffice it to say that evidence enough has been adduced to prove that the judgment has been foretold in both Testaments.
Chapter 30, ¶ 1, line 3

'After the glory' of His Resurrection – a glory **alluded** to in the words: 'Jesus had not yet been glorified' – it was in the person of these Apostles that Jesus was sent to the Gentiles; and this was to be the fulfillment of what the Psalmist had prophesied: 'Thou wilt deliver me from the contradictions of the people; thou wilt make me head of the Gentiles.'
Chapter 30, ¶ 3, line 17

Thus the Gentiles were to become 'prey' in the good sense that they were to be goods **plundered** from the 'strong man,' when he was bound by One still stronger.
Chapter 30, ¶ 3, line 30

The bruised reed he shall not break and the smoking **flax** he shall not quench.
Chapter 30, ¶ 8, line 8

Vocabulary – Write the vocabulary word on the first line (a help for spelling) followed by the definition.

1. Specious

———————— . ———————————————————————

———————————————————————————————————

2. Assent

———————— . ———————————————————————

———————— . ———————————————————————

3. Fettle

———————— . ———————————————————————

———————————————————————————————————

4. Implacable

———————— . ———————————————————————

———————————————————————————————————

5. Inscrutable

———————— . ———————————————————————

———————————————————————————————————

6. Suffice

———————— . ———————————————————————

———————————————————————————————————

7. Alluded

———————— . ———————————————————————

———————————————————————————————————

8. Plundered

———————— . ———————————————————————

———————————————————————————————————

9. Flax

———————— . ———————————————————————

———————————————————————————————————

Memorable Quote

Yet, the hope that hardly anyone but a single thief dying on a cross could entertain is now shared by people everywhere on earth...

- Chapter 30 ¶ 10, page 492

Focus Passages

Book XXI, Chapter 2, (page 495) –

It is not easy to find a proof that will convince unbelievers of the possibility of human bodies remaining not merely active, alive, and uncorrupted after death, but also of continuing forever in the torments of fire. Such unbelievers are deaf to any appeal to the power of the Almighty, and demand a demonstration in terms of positive facts. When facts are reported, they deny the value of the evidence; when the evidence is produced, they declare it inconclusive.

Book XXI, Chapter 7, (page 500) –

Certainly, that explanation is brief enough and, for all I know, sufficient. Why, then, do these skeptics object to our explanation, 'This is the will of Almighty God.' After all, God is the Creator of all natures, and when something seems impossible and incredible and people ask us to explain it, surely, our answer is better than theirs. The whole point of being Almighty is that God has the power to do whatever He wills to do, and He has shown this power in creating so many things that would certainly seem impossible were they not before our very eyes or, at least, testified by reliable witnesses. Some of the examples I have given are known by everybody; others are less well known. As for the marvels recorded in writings but unconfirmed by eye-witnesses, no one can be blamed for disbelief if the writers were men who could easily be wrong and if they wrote without divine intervention.

Book XXI, Chapter 7, (page 501) –

Where marvels of this kind are involved, what better or more cogent explanation can anyone give than to say that it is Omnipotence who has the power and that Omnipotence will use His power of do something which He prophesied in a book in which so many other of His prophesies can be found which have, in fact, been already fulfilled. We must remember that the God who is to do the things which seem impossible is the God who foretold that He will do them, and that this is the same God who made the promise, so clearly fulfilled already, that incredible things would be accepted as credible by incredulous peoples.

Book XXI, Chapter 23, (pages 504 – 505) –

This is not a matter of feeling, but of fact. The fact is that there is no way of waiving or weakening the words which the Lord has told us that He will pronounce in the last judgment: 'Depart from me, accursed ones, into the everlasting fire which was prepared for the devil and his angels.' In this way He showed plainly that it is an eternal fire in which the Devil and his angels are to burn. Then we have the words of the Apocalypse: 'And the devil who deceived them was cast into the pool of fire and brimstone, where also the beast and the false prophet; and they will be tormented day and night for ever and ever.' In the one text we have 'everlasting,' in the other, 'for ever and ever.' These words which have a single meaning in the divine Scripture, namely, of unending duration.

Chapter Summarization

Chapter One

_____

_____

_____

_____

Chapter Two

_____

_____

_____

_____

Chapter Four

_____

_____

_____

_____

Chapter Seven

_____

_____

_____

_____

Chapter Summarization

Chapter Nine

_____

_____

_____

Chapter Twenty-Three

_____

_____

_____

Comprehension Questions

1. In chapter two, what is it that Augustine's opponents refuse to accept?

2. In chapter four Augustine proposes three points relating to human bodies in eternal punishment. What are his three points?

3. In chapter seven Augustine finds no difficulty in believing that God is able to raise bodies from the dead. Why does Augustine find this so easy to believe?

4. In chapter seven Augustine says *the whole point of being Almighty is that God has the power to do whatever He wills to do, and He has shown this power in creating so many things that would certainly seem impossible were they not before our very eyes or, at least, testified by reliable witnesses* (page 500). Do you think Augustine is right that this is *the whole point of being Almighty*?

5. In chapter nine Augustine says there are two kinds of pain a person suffers in eternal punishment. What are the two kinds of pain?

6. To what does Augustine refer in chapter twenty-three as the final and absolute proof of his point that eternal punishment does not end?

7. In chapter twenty-three Augustine is arguing against the idea that the Devil and his angels could ever *return to the life and holiness of the saints*. What is his conclusion?

Vocabulary

The truth is that God, who has endowed things with such a marvelous variety of marvelous qualities that their multitude no longer astonishes us, can give to the substance of flesh the qualities **requisite** for existence in the world to come.

Chapter 4, ¶ 2, line 4

Yet it is bound by no fixed and fast rule; stones, on the contrary, under intense heat become **incandescent**.

Chapter 4, ¶ 3, line 9

You get a similar **anomaly** when dark marks are left by clear oil or when black lines are engraved by white silver.

Chapter 7, ¶ 4, line 12

We must remember that the God who is to do the things which seem impossible is the God who foretold that He will do them, and that this is the same God who made the promise, so clearly fulfilled already, that incredible things would be accepted as credible by **incredulous** peoples.

Chapter 7, ¶ 5, line 28

Surely, that repetition and that **emphatic** warning, coming from divine lips, are enough to make any man tremble.

Chapter 9, ¶ 1, line 18

Certainly, it is not because so many of the Church's saints and Biblical scholars have **begrudged** the Devil and his angles a final cleansing and the beatitude of the kingdom of heaven.

Chapter 23, ¶ 1, line 6

Thus, it is Scripture, **infallible** Scripture, which declares that God has not spared them.

Chapter 23, ¶ 2, line 1

It is from Scripture that we know that God's sentence implies that He 'dragged them down by **infernal** ropes to Tartarus, and delivered them to be tortured and kept in custody for judgment.'

Chapter 23, ¶ 2, line 7

Since this is quite impossible, all those who desire to escape eternal punishment should **desist** from arguing against God and should rather bow in obedience, while yet there is time, to the command of God.

Chapter 23, ¶ 3, line 15

Vocabulary – Write the vocabulary word on the first line (a help for spelling) followed by the definition.

1. Requisite

   _____. _____

   _____

2. Incandescent

   _____. _____

   _____

3. Anomaly

   _____. _____

   _____

4. Incredulous

   _____. _____

   _____

5. Emphatic

   _____. _____

   _____

6. Begrudged

   _____. _____

   _____

7. Infallible

   _____. _____

   _____

8. Infernal

   _____. _____

   _____

9. Desist

   _____. _____

   _____

Memorable Quote

The whole point of being Almighty is that God has the power to do whatever He wills to do, and He has shown this power in creating so many things that would certainly seem impossible were they not before our very eyes or, at least, testified by reliable witnesses.,

– Chapter 7 ¶ 3, page 500

Focus Passages

Book XXII, Chapter 1, (page 507) –

For, it was this same God who, in the beginning, created the universe and filled it with all those things that the eye can see and all those realities which the mind can know. Of all such creations the highest were the spirits to whom He gave the gift of intelligence and the power to behold God and to be filled with His beatitude. These He has linked by a common bond of love in a single society which we call the holy and heavenly City.

Book XXII, Chapter 5, (page 510) –

What is really hard to believe, for anyone who stops to think, is the way the world came to believe. The fishermen whom Christ sent with the nets of faith into the sea of the world were men unschooled in the liberal arts and utterly untrained as far as education goes, men with no skill in the use of language, armed with no weapons of debate, plumed with no rhetorical power. Yet, the catch this handful of fishermen took was enormous and marvelous. They hauled in fish of every sort, not excluding those rare specimens, the philosophers themselves.

Book XXII, Chapter 22, (page 522) –

From this all but hell of unhappiness here on earth, nothing can save us but the grace of Jesus Christ, who is our Saviour, Lord and God. In fact, the very meaning of the name, Jesus, is Saviour, and when we say 'save' we mean, especially, that He saves us from passing from the misery of this mortal life to a still more miserable condition, which is not so much a life as death. It is true that, even in this life on earth, through the intercession of the saints we have many holy comforts and great remedies. Nevertheless, such favors are not always given to those who ask – lest such favors be mistaken for the real purpose of religion, which is felicity in that other life in which all our ills will be no more. What grace is meant to do is to help good people, not to escape their sufferings, but to bear them with a stout heart, with a fortitude that finds its strength in faith.

Book XXII, Chapter 24, (pages 529 – 530) –

No one person could catalogue all of God's bounties. Each of the blessings which I have, as it were, piled up in a heap, contains a multitude of lesser blessings wrapped up within it, and if I were to unfold each of these packages and deal with the blessings in detail I should never end.

And, remember, all these favors taken together are but the fragmentary solace allowed us in a life condemned to misery. What, then, must be the consolations of the blessed, seeing that men on earth enjoy so much of so many and of such marvelous blessings? What good will God not give to those predestined to eternal life, if He gives so much to those who are doomed to death?

Book XXII, Chapter 30, (page 540) –

Who can measure the happiness of heaven, where no evil at all can touch us, no good will be out of reach; where life is to be one long laud extolling God, who will be all in all; where there will be no weariness to call for rest, no need to call for toil, no place for any energy but praise. Of this I am assured whenever I read or hear the sacred song: 'Blessed are they that dwell in thy house, O Lord: they shall praise thee for ever and ever.' Every fiber and organ of our imperishable body will play its part in the praising of God.

Book XXII, Chapter 30, (page 545) –

I am done. With God's help, I have kept my promise. This, I think, is all that I promised to do when I began this huge work. From all who think that I have said either too little or too much, I beg pardon; and those who are satisfied I ask, not to thank me, but to join me in rejoicing and in thanking God. Amen.

Chapter Summarization

Chapter One

_____

_____

_____

_____

Chapter Five

_____

_____

_____

Chapter Eight

_____

_____

_____

Chapter Twenty-Two

_____

_____

_____

Chapter Summarization

Chapter Twenty-Four

_____

_____

_____

_____

Chapter Thirty

_____

_____

_____

_____

Comprehension Questions

1. In chapter one Augustine says that sin is proof of the goodness of our nature. As this sounds like such a strange statement, what does Augustine mean?

2. In chapter five Augustine discusses three "incredibilities" that occurred. What are these incredibilities?

3. In chapter eight Augustine addresses the question of whether or not miracles still occur. What is his conclusion and what is the reason he gives for why miracles may not be as noticed as in Biblical times?

4. In chapter twenty-two Augustine discusses many of the ills that plague humanity, which are, in his opinion, punishments given to mankind. What is the point of such punishments?

5. How, in chapter twenty-two, does Augustine define the *real purpose of religion?* Do you agree with him that this is religion's real purpose?

6. In chapter twenty-four Augustine discusses the blessings that God has given to humanity. What are these blessings?

7. In chapter thirty Augustine discusses seven ages, or days, of world history. What are these ages?

Vocabulary

Either the world has founded its faith in an unseen and incredible occurrence on the fact that no less incredible occurrences not merely took place but were seen to take place; or else the original occurrence was so **palpably** credible that it needed no additional miracles to convince men's minds of its truth.
Chapter 8, ¶ 2, line 6

Worn out with weeping and with no other **recourse**, he thought that the best thing he could do would be to call in an extremely good skillful surgeon from Alexandria, and have him do what he was too angry to let the other surgeons do.
Chapter 8, ¶ 8, line 7

Then, take our very love for all those things that prove so vain and poisonous and breed so many heartaches, troubles, griefs, and fears; such insane joys in discord, strife, and war; such wrath and plots of enemies, deceivers, sycophants; such fraud and theft and robbery; such **perfidy** and pride, envy and ambition, homicide and murder, cruelty and savagery, lawlessness and lust; all the shameless passions of the impure…
Chapter 22, ¶ 1, line 11

No innocence is greater than that of newly baptized children, yet, to give us a lesson in holy **diffidence**, even they are sometimes attacked by demons.
Chapter 22, ¶ 8, line 4

As for the elements of evil, namely, sin which resulted from man's **audacity** and the penalty imposed by God's judgment, I have already said all that the theme of this work requires.
Chapter 24, ¶ 3, line 2

What words can describe the **myriad** beauties of land and sea and sky?
Chapter 24, ¶ 15, line 5

I speak of activity, although, perhaps, I should rather say calm or **repose**.
Chapter 29, ¶ 1, line 6

Scripture has many texts showing that He is the 'salvation of God,' particularly in the words of the **venerable** old man, Simeon, who took the Child in his arms and said: 'Now thou dost dismiss thy servant, O Lord, according to thy word, in peace; because my eyes have seen thy Salvation.'
Chapter 29, ¶ 11, line 7

The conclusion is that, in the everlasting City, there will remain in each and all of us an **inalienable** freedom of the will, emancipating us from every evil and filling us with every good, rejoicing in the inexhaustible beatitude of everlasting happiness, unclouded by the memory of any sin or of sanction suffered, yet with no forgetfulness of our redemption nor any loss of gratitude for our Redeemer.
Chapter 30, ¶ 6, line 7

Vocabulary – Write the vocabulary word on the first line (a help for spelling) followed by the definition.

1. Palpably

_____. _____

_____

2. Recourse

_____. _____

_____

3. Perfidy

_____. _____

_____

4. Diffidence

_____. _____

_____

5. Audacity

_____. _____

_____

6. Myriad

_____. _____

_____

7. Repose

_____. _____

_____

8. Venerable

_____. _____

_____

9. Inalienable

_____. _____

_____

Memorable Quote

He judged it better and more in accord with His power to bring some greater good even out of evil that to permit no evil whatsoever.

– Chapter 1 ¶ 2, page 508

Made in the USA
Lexington, KY
19 March 2012